CLOSURE

(Formerly titled: Better Man Part II)

BRUCE LANGDON

Ok, so I have to make a confession: it is September 27, 2023...and on my commute home from work this evening, I cued up the **evermore** album for my 45-minute ride. So, what's my confession? <u>This was the first time I've ever listened to the **evermore** album.</u> Yup...released on December 11th, 2020 – and this Swiftie literally had not heard it before...(**and all I felt was shame...**). I blame the pandemic. I'd only heard a couple of songs from **folklore** as well! And wouldn't you know it? As I was listening and driving...I realized I had so much more to say!!

I already submitted "Better Man" for publication, but listening to **evermore**, of course, triggered memories of things I wish I'd included in the first book but did not. Who knows where this addendum is going to end up...but to get the **closure** I'm seeking, I feel the need to get it all out. I thought I had, but this is what I get for not listening to Taylor's entire catalog and calling myself a superfan!...

CHAPTER 1

· · · · · · · · ● · · · · · · ·

Closure

Jon and I broke up seven years ago, now. I know 100% I should not be with Jon. So why does he still show up in my (**wildest) dreams**??

On mornings when I wake up from these dreams, I tell myself that it's because we dated for six years, it's just because he was my longest relationship, and there's nothing more to it. He's typically in the dream in the most benign ways – it's not romantic, it's not sexual, we aren't fighting, he's just there. Most of the time, it's set at his house. Sometimes his new boyfriend is in them too, but usually he's not. Sometimes, it's set present-day, sometimes, it's as if we've gone **back in time**. I wake up in a good mood because the dream was humorous (but I pretty much always wake up in a good mood, so that doesn't mean much). But waking up from yet another dream about a distant ex… makes me **crazier…crazier…**and I'd love for it to stop happening. I'm not hung up on Jon. So, typically, I just start my day and keep it moving.

And when I was shipwrecked, I thought of you
In the cracks of light, I dreamed of you
             -**evermore** -Taylor Swift ft/ Bon Iver

What's so funny is on many occasions, I've had a client tell me a similar tale – they've had dreams about their ex, typically a dream from when **we (they) were happy**…and all too often, their next questions to me, their therapist, is "what do you think it means?" - like, "does it mean I don't *actually* love my husband if I'm still dreaming about my ex!?!" Every time a client has relayed such a tale, I lead by making my disclaimer statement: I have no training in dream interpretation, nor am I even sure people should pull any definitive meaning from a dream. I let them know that if, before they went to sleep the previous evening, they knew they loved their husband – then it's likely that has not changed. And for those clients who regularly see a particular ex in their dreams, a bit of exploration in therapy often reveals that, in one way or another, they never got real **closure.**

My mind turns your life into folklore
I can't dare to dream about you anymore...
　　　　　-Gold rush, Taylor Swift

　　　　Somehow, knowing this piece about closure to be true, I never really afford myself the same grace. There've been mornings after Jon showed up in a dream where I've texted him a friendly "hello" with the ulterior motive of making sure he's still alive (as if I have a psychic ability to know he's passed to the other side, like he's visiting me in a dream because he's recently become a ghost...). On very rare occasions, I'll tell him about the dream because I found it amusing or especially vivid. I stress very rarely because he used to explain that (his ex) Rob used to want to tell him about the dreams he'd had in the morning, and he found this to be incredibly annoying. But even with this knowledge, sometimes I can't resist – if the dream was just too funny to keep to myself. And sometimes I preface it with, "I know how much it annoyed you when Rob would do this, but..." **...Mmh, mmh, mh, mh, I can't help myself, I can't help myself...oh oh oh...**lol.
　　　　On February 11th, 2023, around 9 a.m., I sent Jon the following:
　　　　"Hello, JJJOOOONNNN Last night I had a dream that you had to have Blackie and Brownie put down. You also had

gotten 2 replacement chihuahua puppies and a tiny dog that was the size of a hamster. You also had enlisted 4 very attractive young guys to paint your house watermelon-pattern. Guy had moved out in the dream, because when I went to find you to verify you *actually* wanted your house painted like a watermelon, I realized Guy's stuff was gone. I wanted to take a steam shower but you were in there. I went out where the painters were and got stuck on a ledge because 2 of the painters came out the window behind me and couldn't be bothered to backtrack so I could get back in the house. I woke up just before falling off the ledge on the roof.....

My point? How are the dogs??"

*Suggested listen: **happiness** -Taylor Swift

I like to take a Taylor Swift lyric and change it ever so slightly so that it fits my personal story...

I can't make it go away by making you a villain
I guess it's the price I paid for seven years in Heaven
(six)
-**happiness**, Taylor Swift

It's a bit of a stretch to call the relationship with Jon "Heaven".... But if the lyric fits, let it sit...if it doesn't apply, let it fly. And all too often, the lyric fits...

Oh, leave it all behind
Leave it all behind
And there is happiness
-**Happiness**, Taylor Swift

#closure
PS – none of my other ex-boyfriends haunt my dreams. Sometimes I wish one of them would...but I guess they're busy ☺

*Suggested listen: **I wish you would** -Taylor Swift

3

CHAPTER 2

• • • • • • • ● • • • • • •

A Fly on My Wall?

I'm sure many people have broken up in a restaurant or just after leaving one…

I hadn't heard the song **Right where you left me** before writing this, and yet my brain connects it to that evening after dinner, on the ride home from a restaurant near Mayfaire, when I 'patted' Jon's shoulder ever-so-**delicate**ly, with my…uh…closed fist. Followed by our breakup.

Help, I'm still at the restaurant
Still sitting in a corner I haunt
Cross-legged in the dim light
They say, "What a sad sight,"
I stayed there.
      -Right where you left me, Taylor Swift

But no worries…I'm not there anymore. I'm at a drag show in Myrtle Beach, enjoying the **cruel summer**time sadness performed by this gorgeous busty brunette. (Luv you, Nick!) Lol

Oh jeez, I'm now going to derail into something that no one ever has to know…but if I'm really telling on myself like I initially said I was planning to…I guess I've got to tell this part, too.

4

CHAPTER 3

• • • • • • • • • • • •

This is Embarrassing

I had moved to Raleigh (without Jon) with the understanding that I should be returning after my nine-month internship wrapped up. The internship led to me being hired for a post-master's fellowship, which meant staying on at The Center, but which was also a time-limited role. I was making the drive back to the beach most weekends, visiting Jon and the doggies. I thought things were going well between us…until I caught him 'with his pants down' when I had come to town to give him his birthday present.

Learning that Jon was fucking dudes behind my back was a painful realization. I felt dumb because I hadn't been fucking anyone in Raleigh. Part of me wished I had been because I figured maybe then I'd be less angry about his indiscretions. And while the thing about me being celibate in Raleigh was true, what I left out was why.

At The University Counseling Center where I'd earned my spot as a post-master's fellow, a crop of new interns rolled in. And one of these interns was fucking **gorgeous.** Like, I-can't-talk-to-this-guy-he's-too-attractive-and-I'll-just-stutter-and-look-stupid level gorgeous. So, for a minute there, I didn't talk to him. Working as a counselor can be a rather insular activity, so avoiding him was not a problem. We had offices in different areas of The Counseling Center. I could see him in a staff meeting and just not look at him. This would be no problem…

But unfortunately, this handsome motherfucker is also captivating. Engaging. Infectious.

And he was befriending _my_ friends who also worked there and who inhabited the surrounding offices. My plan was going to fail – I could hear him laughing with one of my colleagues, Rayna, in her office, and I realized he was just too fucking nice for me to keep avoiding him forever.

When we did speak, I had a 'shield' – and thank goodness for that. Not that he would be interested in me – I don't mean to sound cocky. It was just nice to know that since Jon and I were still together at this part of my story, I could drop the "I have a boyfriend. He lives a couple of hours away. I go to see him every weekend..." fact. So, I got to auto-shield myself from any sexual harassment charges I may have incurred if Nick thought I was single. Because had Nick expressed even the slightest interest in finding out if our office walls were soundproof...the fun way...I would've made _really_ bad decisions. (Think: **Look what you made me do...**)

I also got to shield myself from the rejected feelings I'd inevitably feel if I ever got the guts to tell him that the more we spent time together, the more I wished he was **mine.** And the less I thought about Jon.

Fortunately, there was an additional barrier to me ever letting Nick know any of the feelings I was feeling. He had a boyfriend of two years. Jon and I had been together for about six at this point. And I was not trying to be a home wrecker, nor was I trying to complicate things with Jon any more than they already were complicated. But damn, I was crushing on this dude, badly.

Nick is tall, dark, and handsome. His mom is Venezuelan, and his dad was white. He used to talk about being on a 'cutting cycle' when, a couple of weeks before, he'd been shoveling microwaved lasagna into his mouth, burning the shit out of the roof of it. I think that was the same day he put his glasses on my face as I was looking out a window at The Center. "Holy shit, that tree has _individual_ branches!" Before that, I thought my vision was 20/20.

6

CLOSURE

Whenever Nick and I both ended up on breaks at The Center, we would hang out. I was invited to meet his friends outside of work so we could chill and watch Ru Paul's Drag Race as a group and break up the weekday monotony. This was always a lot of fun. A casual pot-luck style opportunity to hang out with cool people...and be around Nick.

****

Total Tangent Time:

When I was socializing my chihuahua puppies, it was Nick's group of friends (who also became some of my close friends) that did a lot towards making them super friendly. After all, they are chihuahuas – I think by nature they're supposed to be yippy and overprotective (/**mean**) towards unfamiliar people...but not mine!

Also, on the topic of the dogs, I hadn't initially thought getting two of them was a smart move. One dog would be plenty! I found Pebbles on a puppy-finding website, and fell in love, largely because she looked so much like another dog that had my heart (Brownie). But Pebbles was in a town five hours away from Raleigh, so getting to her was a challenge since I worked five days a week at The Center. Plus, she was expensive ($500 – which early in my career as a therapist was way more than I needed to be spending. Keep in mind I moved to Raleigh for an unpaid internship). The distance problem could be resolved if I was willing to pay another $200 to a dog-delivery guy and meet him halfway. $700 was too much money! Not to mention, I had to work the next day, so there was only so far I could drive...So it was not looking like Brownie's mini-doppelgänger would work out after all.

I jumped on Craigs List to see if there was an alternate chihuahua that could become my new buddy.

That's when I came across a few motion blurred photos of a deer headed chihuahua puppy that looked really cute.

Of course, I was judging mostly by photos taken when her head was whipping around excitedly, so much so that it was tricky to assess what she really looked like. But what I *could* tell was that she was only an hour-and-a-half away in Randleman, NC, and she was going for $200. This felt like the obvious choice. All of the chihuahuas I'd known and loved up to this point had been apple-head chihuahuas, but I wasn't going to write her off over her deer-head shape! That would just be silly. Plus, she shared a birthday with my colleague from The Counseling Center, Rayna, and my (former best) friend, Rob. All three have a birthday of 4/12, with my own being the inverse of theirs. Talk about a sign! And so, I headed to Randleman to meet my new puppy.

It was on the way to pick up Puppy#1 that the puppy breeder offered to drop the price of Pebbles by $100. Then, the dog delivery man also shaved $100 off his delivery fee and said he'd be happy to meet up in Randleman, NC. And so, I had two puppies lined up to be my new sidekicks.

I picked up Puppy#1 from a nice woman living in a trailer park. Fortunately, this puppy was, in fact, insanely cute. The woman explained that as hard as they'd tried to get her to stay still to take photos, she was just too energetic and excitable to keep her head still that long. And yes, she was...and is. Which factored into my initial decision to name this little puppy "Spazz." Pebbles was advertised as "Pebbles #3." **I spy with my little tired eye, tiny as a firefly, a Pebbles that we picked up last July. -Sweet Nothing**, Taylor Swift. (*technically*, I picked her up in June...)

I realized, rather swiftly, that I was in over my head. Two dogs were too much for me to handle! What was I thinking? So, I began contemplating my next move, deciding I should simply re-post "Spazz" on Craigs List for $200 - the same amount I bought her for. I mean, even though she was super cute and the two got along well, Spazz was a unique challenge. I explained to Nick what I'd been thinking...that

Spazz had to go because "she's just such a handful! She wants my attention ALL THE TIME! She's so hyperactive, she wants to be around me 24/7, she has no "off" switch...She's sweet, but I don't think I can deal with the constant licking, the wanting to be up in my space...her intense energy...it's too much!" Nick's response?

"So...she's behaving like a puppy?"

Damn. I think I tried to plead my case a bit more, but all he responded with was "...sounds like a puppy...". Yeah, yeah, yeah...I get it.

But he was right. I got what I signed up for. Just because Pebbles was a bit more chill, Spazz was just being a puppy.

And then Nick alerted me that Spazz was not a name I could let stick, even if the shoe fit. We were over at one of those Ru Paul's Drag Race get-togethers with the puppies when he started brainstorming names. When he said "Layla," I knew it was meant to be. Seven years later, she's still a spazz, but she's a lot more loveable as a Layla. And I'm glad both Layla and Pebbles are still with me and that Layla doesn't know that I almost sent her off to be someone else's cute, little, energetic and adorable nightmare.

TOTAL TANGENT TIME OVER

****

CHAPTER 4

·······•··•·•·······

About Break-Ups

Despite my own sticky, messy break-up history, there is some knowledge I've gained through working with therapy clients and through paying attention in my personal life, and it feels like it's worth noting:

Often, people may feel guilty for breaking up with their partner, even if they know in their heart it's the right thing to do and it needs to happen. Especially in relationships where a couple has become a bit codependent and a rift between themselves and their friends/support network has developed. That drive to support your dumped partner may feel like the *kind* thing to do, but I'd argue it is not. You cannot break someone's heart and then stick around to help them mend it. You can't be your ex's shoulder to cry on...I mean, I get why people want that to work – I've just seen a lot of evidence that it doesn't. (**Never a clean break, no one there to save me...**) A clean break – or at least significant space - is kind of how it has to be – it forces both newly single people to rebuild their social support networks and reconnect with friends who may have drifted somewhat while the person was in a relationship. Or to make new friends. Most true friends will make peace with the distance that happened while you were in a relationship - if it's a true friendship, they will welcome you back.

If I can give some more crucial advice, I'd say that – especially for young people – when you get into a new relationship, do your best to keep up with your friends! If a break-up happens, you're going to need them! Unfortunately, that falls on deaf ears all-too-often with college-aged adults.

But often, your friends are your best eyes and ears in case a relationship is toxic, whether you want to see it/hear it or not.

Finally, on the topic of break-ups, I would discourage anyone from staying with someone solely because of the years you've already put into a relationship. If that's literally the main reason you're holding onto...don't. I've done this before. And I've worked with therapy clients who do it even when they know they're unhappy and attempts at fixing the communication issues aren't getting them anywhere. A lot of people stay with a significant other because they're afraid to be alone (even for a little bit) or fearful of the feelings they'll experience if they go through a break-up. I'd argue that if you know it isn't going to work and it's not likely to get any better, you're doing yourself and your partner a favor by going your separate ways. Especially in situations where you aren't married and have no kids to factor in...what're you waiting for? (Note: this is not my advice for anyone who hasn't tried to have more challenging conversations about communication or getting your needs met by your partner. Leaving a relationship without telling your partner you're dissatisfied is just a cop-out – that's different and not what I'm talking about...And if you can't have these more sensitive conversations with a partner, go to therapy!) When you stick with a partner for all the wrong reasons, when it does end, you'll likely regret not doing it sooner. (DV and other sticky situations probably have a less straightforward exit strategy, so if safety is of concern, the above suggestions should not be applied without considering all complicating factors first. Stay safe!)

CHAPTER 5

•••••••• • •• •••••••

A Hundred Thrown-Out Speeches I Almost Said to You

Back to the story…why did I throw a random chapter about break-ups in there, you may be wondering? Well, because it was at this part of the story that I drove the two-hour trek east for the weekend to spend time with Jon. And it was this weekend in particular that I finally snapped, and six years of living under the threat that **we are never ever ever ever getting back together** was finally over. I broke up with Jon…and I high-tailed it to Myrtle Beach.

*Suggested listen: **Breathe** -Taylor Swift

In Myrtle Beach, I got to spend time around Nick and his group of friends who had traveled from Raleigh and other areas of North Carolina for the Quest: Sober on the Beach weekend. Nick's boyfriend was also there. This wasn't the first time we'd met or anything, but this was the first time I realized he was actually a decent guy…but of course he was. I should've known Nick wouldn't be dating anything less. After all, Nick is awesome.

Since I'd come to Myrtle Beach on a whim and the rest of the crew had all planned to be there for the weekend, I was going to have to find somewhere to stay. And being the gentlemen they were, Nick and his boyfriend offered to let me stay in their hotel room with them. At that moment, I could not think of anywhere I would get a more miserable night's sleep…so for reasons they did not understand, I shot that idea down quick and found my own hotel room elsewhere. After all, the slightest bit of PDA between those two could have sent me spinning out – I was embarrassingly hung up on Nick-a-licious …(he's familiar with my nicknaming ways…), who I'd just seen do drag, and somehow I was even more attracted to him. I definitely thought seeing this masc dude I was crushing on do drag would be a boner killer, but Nick owned that stage and refused to get the fuck out of my head. But I kinda liked it…

When the weekend came to a close, and I was back at The Counseling Center, another post-masters fellow casually asked in a group meeting, "How's Jon doing? Did you see him over the weekend?" - and so I told everyone we'd broken up. I am generally a private person, and I really did not want to talk to anyone about it. Everyone knowing we'd broken up was fine – but we were there to provide therapy to students! There was no room for my own emotions!…and I liked it that way.

Two weeks later at The Counseling Center, Nick – the thunder stealer - informed a colleague and myself that he had broken up with his boyfriend. Wait…what?!? It was news to me that they'd had any friction at all, really…but Nick opened up about the boyfriend's issues with binge drinking and how Nick being sober meant that they just weren't meant to be. Nick also mentioned that their sex life had been less than spectacular. Again, if I hadn't been fighting myself to NOT sexually harass this man for months at this point, there is no telling what suggestive or slutty thing I may have blurted out…

"so…you haven't gotten off in…how long?" **#I wish you would…**

Nick was at The Counseling Center from Fall 2015- Summer 2016. My 'code' of values prevented me from ever giving him either of the first two letters I penned late at night since we both had significant others and all. But for this 3rd letter, we were both single. But I still never gave it to him…And while this one doesn't include a date, it was probably written sometime in the summer of 2016…

Nick-tastic!

As I begin this letter, I'm already thinking I shouldn't be writing it. I guess my biggest fear in sharing any of what I'm about to write is that it could alter our friendship. I don't want anything to be any different than it is right now. If possible, I'd like you to read this and – in a perfect world – forget its contents. I'm basically saying what I am because I find myself having emotions about something that's really none of my concern, and I'm aware of why, but you are not & that feels unfair.

Alright….so where the fuck is this going..?

(I feel sooo pathetic for writing this down…I've done a really good job of keeping it to myself…) Alright – so the thing is, I have feelings for you. I hoped they would have gone away by now, but they have not. This is not a new development – I have known I felt this way since long before I broke up with Jon. Which also means I can be your friend – and just a friend – without it causing any issues. Well, until recently…

So I'm really not telling you this because I have some expectations that we are going to be together. I am telling you this because I feel myself getting overly worked up about you talking to guys that suck. This sounds <u>really</u> cheesy, but I've given a lot of thought to how well I would treat you if you were my boyfriend. So watching you text guys like Hugh & 'X-mas sweater' – both of whom you have said are underwhelming to say the least – bothers me in a way that I wish it didn't. It's none of my business who you hook up with or date, but as a friend, I'm going to want you to be with someone who treats you well and who appreciates all of the awesome things about you that I appreciate. I will have to get over the fact that my skin crawls when you mention hooking up with anyone because that's not your problem. I didn't feel like it was fair to keep interjecting my opinions about your sex life without being completely honest. I do wish you a happy & healthy relationship with someone amazing, & if you need to hook up with a ton of people that suck before you are ready to settle down, then so be it. But keep in mind that guys like Christmas Sweater will develop feelings for you quick, & if you're just looking for a blow job, then you're kinda being as ass hole by leading him on...right?

**So that's where the letter I was writing ends abruptly. I think I stopped writing because I realized it was heading in a manipulative direction when all I really wanted to say to him had been said in the first couple of paragraphs.

Nick and I are still friends to this day, and all these years later, he knows nothing of the feelings I had for him. Who knows what could have been if only I'd shut the door to his office and told him to take his fucking pants off. Lol, I could have derailed both of our therapy careers just to get some dick. But truly, I fought my desire to stare at this man really hard (really...really hard...) because sexually harassing him would just be too easy. And if he was too easy, well, we'd have been fired. I am not quiet. And I have no doubt Nick would not disappoint. But rather than derail this story into a fantasy land, I'm sticking to the truth...although it is tempting to go the other route...

The letter above reminds me of a feeling I haven't felt in a really long time. That feeling where another person makes the butterflies wake up, and your heart beat becomes audible in your ears when you see that person standing across the room. And if he starts walking towards you with a smile on his face, you get worried you're just going to randomly start blushing for no explainable reason. I have a hate/love relationship with this feeling. And around Nick, I had to play it cool – after all, I was further along in the journey we were both on as licensed counselors...so I had boundaries to uphold. And **a hundred thrown out speeches I almost said to** him...and three letters that just never got sent.

CHAPTER 6

••••••• • ••••••••

Nothing New

As a quick refresher: I broke up with Jon and was doing my best not to have to think about it or talk with anyone about it, especially when I was at work. Then, just two weeks later, Nick announced he had broken up with his beau. And Nick was not quite as filtered when it came to processing his breakup. The above letter was undoubtedly written a couple of months after Nick's breakup. At some point, I remember thinking internally, "shut up about what's-his-face already and notice what's right in front of you...**ME!**" I also remember getting annoyed because even though I had no interest in airing my dirty laundry with my peers, Nick was more of an outward processor. Part of me was thinking, "I was with Jon for six years, and I'm sitting here sad about our **castles crumbling**, but you don't hear me going on and on about it...and I'm sure Jon was a far more terrible boyfriend than yours!..." Lol. Luckily, these were all internal thoughts that I found myself having. Under just about any circumstance, I am a great friend to have because I will listen to someone sharing a struggle they're having all day long. But when the dude I'd been sweating for months suddenly became single immediately after I had, only for his ex-boyfriend to be all he could talk about, I was having difficulty hearing it. Prior to their break-up, **I forgot that** he **existed** was an easily achievable mindset I had fallen into because Nick barely mentioned him. So yeah...let's just say this was disheartening.

But I kept all of these thoughts locked inside. I cared a lot about Nick, and he was hurting. So I had to let go of my wishful thinking that his break-up had been timed intentionally in response to me becoming single. I needed to be a friend, and (stuff my own feelings and) listen. After all, Nick and I were newly practicing therapists. Plus, I realized I could listen to him talk about anything…so long as I just stared at his lips and tuned out the words. It didn't hurt when I did that.

I knew enough to know that it would be way too weird to let Nick know I was feeling any of this and then have to face him every day at The Counseling Center. No matter how he responded – that just would've been messy. In reality, there was no actual difference in terms of a power dynamic at The Center between him and me, but in my mind, I just concluded that as long as we worked together, I had to put these feelings into a box and shove them down…And just continue hanging out with my new friend, who was quickly becoming a really close, if not a best friend. There was PG-level flirting between us because Nick is generally flirtatious. There was more of it before his breakup, so this development sucked on multiple levels. I realized it wasn't fair of me to feel hurt when he'd talk about his ex – and it wasn't fair of me to be jealous when he started talking about other dudes he'd been 'seeing' casually. Or to be jealous of the girl he started sleeping with. But it didn't change the fact that those feelings were there.

We could call it even, you could call me babe for the weekend…?
    -**'tis the damn season,** Taylor Swift

CHAPTER 7

·······●·●·●·●·······

Confusion & foreshadowing

*Suggested listen: **Foolish one** -Taylor Swift

Sometimes, when people don't properly deal with their feelings, they come out in ways you don't mean for them to What I mean is, by not properly dealing with my feelings, they were bound to come out in a way that was regrettable, to say the least…

…And if you wanted me, you really should've showed…
But we were something, don't you think so?
Roaring twenties, tossing pennies in the pool

(*I was 29 when I met Nick. Just *a couple of* months shy of my 30th birthday…like I said, if the lyric fits.)

And if my wishes came true
It would've been you…
~~~~~~~~~~~~~~~~~
But it would've been fun
If you would've been the one.
    -The 1, Taylor Swift

*Suggested listen: **The 1** -Taylor Swift

Crushing on Nick + Ending my own relationship + Listening to Nick talk excessively about his ex …then running into Nick's ex @ a nightclub when the ex was drunk as fuck = A big mess…

CLOSURE

…scared to see the ending…??…
…look what you made me do….??…
Nah, nothing <u>that</u> crazy…
Don't worry, I **didn't do **something bad.** Well,
not *that* bad, anyway…

I didn't have it in myself to go with grace
And so the battleships will sink beneath the waves…
-my tears ricochet, Taylor Swift

**If you're wondering how these seemingly unrelated
songs by Taylor Swift can come together to make sense in a
set of circumstances, it will make sense soon enough…

CHAPTER 8

••••••• • •••••••

You Can Find Me in the Club

My friend Lee came in from out of town for the weekend. He hated the town that the shipping company he worked for had gotten him to move to, so every weekend, he took off to either Raleigh or DC just to maintain his sanity. And lucky for me, this weekend he'd made the <u>right</u> choice!- he was coming to see me in Raleigh. He would stay at my apartment when he came into town and 'sleep' on my couch. Sometimes, I'd pass out with him. Other times, I'd be asleep in my bedroom. Sometimes, I'd be hooking up with someone in my bedroom while he was hooking up in the living room…it was a very 'anything-goes' type 'sleeping' arrangement. Only once did he and I have sex…in Raleigh, at least. But anyway…Lee was someone I considered to be one of my best friends. I'd gotten close with him when I was still dating Jon. At that time, Lee regularly visited Jon and me on the weekends. Since he didn't like where he'd been stationed and had no interest in sticking around for barn parties or whatever it is they do in tiny towns of North Carolina over the weekends. I was happy to have him there with me in Raleigh any time he wanted to visit.

So, on this particular weekend night, Lee and I were going out to Legends, the gay nightclub in downtown Raleigh. Clubbing had long been a shared interest of ours. [*In time, Lee came to really like where he's living…which is why he's still there! But for the longest time, he kept reporting he was depressed, didn't know anyone, and every day was misery until he got to travel to see friends on weekends. And Lee is a super social person, so small-town living was an adjustment, to say the least.]

It was a fairly typical night out at the club – dancing, running around, talking to people…dancing, sweating, Lee laughing at me any time a Britney Spears or **Taylor Swift** song came on (he knew my weaknesses well)…and – oh yeah, dancing. (*Dancing freely – not **with our hands tied**…)

We were having a blast, as we always did.

At some point during the evening, I crossed paths with Nick's ex, who was clearly intoxicated. I thought to myself, "Oh! <u>This</u> is what Nick meant when he said this dude had a problem with *binge* drinking…" In the few times I'd seen this person, he'd been sober. Watching Ru Paul's Drag Race with Nick and his *amazing* crew of friends from AA, "Matt" had shown up a couple of times late and stayed fairly quiet. But this was not the "Matt" from previous encounters. For lack of a more perfect descriptor, this was 'sloppy "Matt." 'If you're wondering why his name keeps showing up in 'quotes', it's because when we crossed paths, I said, "oh, hey Matt!" **this man's name is not Matt. I totally called him by the wrong name. I knew as soon as it came out of my mouth that was not his name…but I couldn't remember what it actually was…

Luckily, he was far too drunk to catch me misnaming him. I introduced him quickly to my buddy, Lee, which led to "Matt" unknowingly solving the riddle in my head. {But for the purposes of this story, he will just continue to be "Matt."} After the brief intro, Lee and I kept it moving, and "Matt" stumbled on to wherever he'd been heading.

As the night was winding down, once again, we crossed paths with "Matt." No less intoxicated than the last time we'd seen him, I asked him if he needed a ride home. I cannot remember if he'd taken an Uber to the club or if he'd driven, but whatever the case was, I knew I could get him home safely. After all, Nick had loved this guy at one point, and even though it was a dagger to my heart any time Nick mentioned that fact, I still wanted him to get home safely.

Loaded up in my car with Lee in the passenger seat and "Matt" in the back, we headed to the address "Matt" provided. He lived relatively close to the club, so it was a short ride. During the car ride, "Matt" began propositioning Lee, suggesting he come in and spend the night. I'm certain I had given Lee a brief overview of the situation before we left the club – that this sloppy dude was someone who I had to get home safely because he mattered to someone who mattered to me.

Lee was a grown man, and he could sleep with whoever he wanted to. But despite his ever-ready libido, Lee said something like, "... Nah, I've gotta go home with Bruce." "Matt" replied, as he was getting out of the car, "aww, come on!... He can come too!" I let "Matt" know that we both knew that was an absolutely terrible idea for obvious reasons. I'm sure Matt smelled what I was stepping in, even if he was pretty drunk. Nick would go absolutely ballistic, and he knew that (I'm sure...). I also knew that "Matt" was someone my brain had managed to suppress so well that his name was never lodged into my memory bank - mostly because I wanted to marry his ex-boyfriend. But also, I wasn't into him any more than he was into me. He just wanted to hook up with Lee...maybe because Lee was cute...maybe because "Matt" was just drunk as hell...and maybe because some part of him hoped I'd tell Nick, as "Matt" knew who my loyalty was to.

Fortunately, Lee's denial of consent held firm, and "Matt" made it into his house, safely.

[Side note: I didn't know Lee ever said "no" to sex with a cute guy. Whether it was because he didn't want to sleep with a word-slurring drunk, or because he knew this was my friend's recent ex, or if he already had someone from Grindr coming over later – I have no idea. But the next time someone gets it twisted and thinks sluts don't have morals and standards, think again! (Lee and I also had <u>that</u> in common, lol. Yes...all of that.)]

CHAPTER 9

••••••• ● •••••••

Now I see daylight

Monday morning at The Counseling Center, as soon as I got a chance to be around Nick, I started to tell him, "I saw "Matt" at the club Saturday night…I feel bad, but I called him the wrong name…but he was drunk as fuck, so I don't think he caught it…" Nick cut me off right there. "I don't want to hear any more about it." I was fine with discontinuing this topic of conversation. All I'd been wanting for months now was for Nick never to want to talk about this guy again…**like…ever.**

CHAPTER 10

· · · · · · • • • · · · · ·

If you asked me if I loved him…I'd lie.

Nick, as downtown Raleigh's very best unpaid tour guide, knew all of the best places to eat. He knew how to get anywhere downtown on foot without any GPS checking or second-guessing himself. He knew historic information about *this* building…or *that* statue. He knew where to get the best desserts, what was being discussed in the government buildings we walked by, and what would be built on the construction site that was just a fenced-in area and a bunch of concrete at the time he mapped out for me the future plans of the city. He loved Raleigh and could enthusiastically tell me all of the reasons why. He knew the city so well that when I asked him how much further he would make me walk in Raleigh's summer heat, I figured I could trust his response when he said, "oh, just one more block, down this way…" Nick was a captivating conversationalist, so much so that it wasn't until a quarter mile later that I realized I'd been duped. Nick had taken me somewhere downtown that had been fenced and boarded as far as the eye could see…so with no way to cut through to where we needed to go, "one block" stretched on indefinitely. I might've been irritated by his playing dumb - like he didn't know this area was under construction from the minute we made that turn - but it meant I got to spend more time with him. **#LuckyOnes**

CLOSURE

Wherever you stray I follow
I'm beggin' for you to take my hand, wreck my plans,
yeah that's my man.

-**willow**, Taylor Swift

Don't get it twisted - I did not think Nick felt any of what I was feeling. That being said, sometimes it can be fun to think of what could have been and that **maybe this thing was a masterpiece, 'til** I blew it all up. (**...next chapter.**)

*Suggested listen: **Teardrops on My Guitar** -Taylor Swift

CHAPTER 11

·········•●●•·········

...It actually hurts

It must've been **August** when this next part happened because that's Nick's birth month, and we were going to dinner after work to celebrate his birthday...hell, maybe this happened on his birthday. I'm not sure – but it makes it even worse if it was, so let's pretend it definitely wasn't his actual birthday...

After work, our friend and colleague Rayna, Nick, and I were heading downtown for an early dinner at the restaurant Nick chose. Rayna and I were seated next to one another on the Booth side of the small table, with Nick in a chair across from us. We had only been seated a short while and were doing the look-over-your-menu-while-making-small-talk thing when Nick **brought him up**...(eye roll...I thought we were done with this...)...

I do not even remember what Nick was saying about "Matt" in that moment...but **loose lips sink ships all the damn time**, right? My dumbass just turned to Rayna and started retelling the Cliff's Notes version of my encounter with "Matt" at the club...

"I just recently ran into "Matt" out at Legends. He was drunk as fuck...slurring his words. If he had driven, it would've been BAD, so me and my friend drove him home afterwards..."Matt" tried to fuck my friend when we got to his house, but Lee was <u>not</u> interested. Matt was so trashed..."

This was NOT the right way to set the tone for a fun birthday dinner. I just remember thinking *before* I spoke that I just wanted Nick to stop talking about "Matt" once and for all. What I did not want was for Nick to become furious at me. I'd never even seen him mad before. I remember *after* I said this, I immediately knew I'd fucked up – I knew that before I looked at Nick's face...and yep, sure enough. Confirmation. I was a total asshole. I think Nick said something to me before storming out of the restaurant, but I don't remember what. I wish he'd punched me in the face. Because Nick did absolutely nothing wrong, and I just assaulted him with a story that he'd made clear to me the first time I tried to tell it that he didn't want to hear it.

Nick should've punched me in the face. But he didn't. I never would have wanted to hurt this guy's feelings. And pissing him off was not on that evening's itinerary...but it happened. And it was my fault.

This effectively killed the **fairytale** I'd concocted in my head, where Nick and I would someday live happily ever after.

He forgave me. And he and I existed in the full-time 'friend zone' from that day forward. This was a lot more comfortable for me, if I'm being honest. Having a huge crush on someone whom you're maintaining a close friendship with and who is also a coworker and who has no idea is NOT fun.

As I type this, it's funny, thinking, "...and *that's* when I put Nick in the FRIEND ZONE." Meanwhile, Nick reads this, thinking, "...Bruce...no offense, but you've *only ever* been in my friend zone..." Lol.

I love Nick - super platonically - to this day.

And if he reads this and decides he *should* punch me in the face, after all...there's no statute of limitations on that, at least not in my book. (hah, literally and figuratively)

Nick continued to be a colleague of mine. Hell, I ended up getting him to join the private practice I found myself working for after we had both left The University Counseling Center. But by that point, the romantic feelings I had were gone.

We have a whole bunch of other 'friend memories' from this point forward, but this book isn't about friendships, so…to Nick, I say (lovingly…) **bye bye, baby!**

*Suggested listen: **August** -Taylor Swift

A part of me still wishes this all had gone very differently, and the following chapters were all about the amazing adventures we had, both in the bedroom and in the unfortunate moments between when he wore clothes. Nick used to describe himself as border-lite, and if anyone with a background in psychology or with friends who are diagnosed with BPD, yes, he meant (jokingly) exactly what you may be picturing. Intensely emotional with tatted-up muscle arms and a smile that melted me through much of my time working at The Center. I never wear underwear, and the number of times he'd leave my office and I'd have leaked through my khakis was highly problematic. Also, Nick said if I was going to use his name, the smut level better make it a worthwhile read…ahahahahaha. I let him know it was a missed opportunity to be the main character in an amazingly graphic sexcapade. But he's living his best life out in California now…so all I am left with is the fantasy of what could have been. It's probably better that we never fucked – he'd probably still be zip tied to some furniture in one of my bedrooms. And in my fantasy land, he's on board with that. (Love you, Nick!)

CHAPTER 12

•••••••●••••••

Gorgeous

At the risk of creating the most disjointed narrative of all time, a memory was just triggered when the song **"Gorgeous"** started playing on my phone just now. So, let me set the scene…

Rewind it back to my relationship with Jon, and imagine a time when **we were happy.** Because when we were happy, I was, admittedly, the biggest weirdo boyfriend ever. I used to walk around the house talking about "The cutest little baby man, cutest man in all the land…" I would say his name in all sorts of weird inflections and tones, in an array of different voices. And I am a nicknaming motherfucker, let me tell ya. "JC Buckets" (because if anyone remembers the Mr. Buckets toy commercials, "the balls pop out of his mouth!" I don't know, I thought it was funny…) – that's just one example from a long list of nicknames, said with affection, that this man was gifted by his silly boyfriend.

We used to laugh. A lot. Sometimes I forget that, but we did.

Anyway, where am I going with this? Oh yeah!

Another one of my quirks that Jon had to survive was me talking about "THAT FACE!!" I used to say, starting off in a soft voice, "…I'm not sure if there has ever been anything as gorgeous…as…THAT FACE!!" I'd say weird-ass things like, "Now, has anyone ever told you that you have the all-time cutest little-baby-man face??!? Seriously, I think people are scared to tell you, but THAT FACE!!…" I'd say these things regularly when it was just the two of us. Because I sure as hell didn't want to announce to just anybody that I was in possession of something so precious…(…wait for it…)….THAT FACE!!

So, fast forward through my relationship with Jon, past the break-up, to 2017 when Taylor came out with the song "**Gorgeous**", and I heard, for the first time, lyrics that helped me to feel a bit less like I was a weirdo….

You're so gorgeous
I can't say anything to your FACE…
'Cause look at THAT **FACE!!**

I have never shared with Jon that this song makes me laugh when I sing the lyrics *my* way (Bruce's Version..? lol) and think about THAT FACE!

I'd be shocked if Jon has ever heard this song…but it does make me laugh at my own ridiculousness, and it brings back fond memories of that part of our relationship.

(On an unrelated note: Jon, like the dude from the song **Gorgeous,** has **ocean blue eyes**.)

Part of why I never made Jon listen to **Gorgeous** in 2017 after it was released was because he had a lot bigger things going on in his world. Jon was arrested on May 31st, 2017, when USPS intercepted a few ounces of meth he'd ordered off the dark web. Jon and I broke up over a year before his arrest, and with him living a couple of hours away, only a few people in Raleigh mentioned it to me. No one asked anything about my own meth use, past or present. If they had, I can't imagine I would have been honest about it, anyway.

I sent Jon an email checking to make sure he was okay on June 2nd, 2017. He noted in his response that he now understood why I'd been dreading turning myself in each weekend for jail time, which resulted from my arrest back in 2013. Jon said in his email, "…I should be ok. Fortunately I have the ability to pay the staggering cost of defending myself which is great for me but it seems so unfair to all the poor souls stuck in the system with much smaller charges. I'll be fine one way or the other. Thanks again for your thoughts and tell everyone I'm a-ok." In the end, Jon was right – he ended up on probation but had enough money to avoid any major consequences, like jail time.

CHAPTER 13

•••••••• • ••••••••

Friends with an Ex?

Absolutely! There is a recipe for success that allows ex's to be friends, of course! Time and space are often crucial for this to work, assuming it was a meaningful relationship. Because no one should see their recent ex – who they're maintaining a 'friendship' with – date someone new, up close, especially if there are any lingering or complicated feelings. Now, whether I'm pulling this little tidbit from rom-coms I've seen, from personal experience, from hearing hundreds of people's romantic experiences during my time as a therapist (or it's just coming from the Library of "Duh..."), I'd advise anyone who wants advice to not put themselves in a situation where they're pretending like this feels '**perfectly fine,**' and they're 'cool with it...' With a healthy amount of healing and space, people can, and often do, eventually find a sense of **happiness** knowing their ex is happy with someone else. (Think: Gwen Stefani: *Cool*, style.) You, too, <u>can</u> be that evolved of a person...*some day*. But if a break-up with someone significant happened in the past year, do yourself a huge favor and steer clear! (I don't know why the hell I'm rhyming...like I'm running out of timing? I promise to stop now).

I don't know if there's any evidence to support this statement scientifically, but I was once told by someone who works in mental health that it takes about half the time you were in a relationship to heal from the break-up of the relationship. I'm throwing that out there, despite the lack of evidence to back it up, merely to suggest that you shouldn't rush *healing*. I've met with so many people who have come to therapy insisting, "My friends don't want to hear another word about my break-up!" Well, if that's the case, then welcome to therapy - you're in the right place. And I'm glad you have friends who are willing to tell you directly that they have met their quota for listening capacity. Most friends will get you through the worst of it. And there's a very real chance you'll be able to return the favor someday. Because everyone experiences grief – whether it's a romantic relationship or the death of someone significant.

[Side note: I have already accepted that my very best friend in the whole world may talk about the death of her cat – a majestic Devon Rex named Vincent Crookshanks – for the rest of our lives. And for her, if she does, I will **tolerate it**. Because I love her. But I also know enough about grief to know she's doing it properly. Vincent didn't pass away all that long ago, so for her to be speaking about him from a place of acceptance and recognizing her strength and resilience as she heals, I don't have any concerns that she's getting hung up in any way as she processes his passing.

Britt was just in town visiting me, and so I wanted to find a place to shamelessly plug her into the story. Of course, if she ever takes the whiskers of his that she collected over the years to Korea and pays hundreds of thousands of dollars to have him cloned, I will be editing this paragraph significantly…lol]

CHAPTER 14

·······•·•·•·······

Happiness After You...

I hope she'll be a beautiful fool, who takes my spot next to you is a great lyric. I used to tell Jon when we would fight that whoever he dated after me would need to be <u>really</u> dumb to put up with all of his bullshit. So, are Taylor and I essentially saying the same thing? *It matters because I think this may be the only advice I ever gave Jon that he actually took...

   ...*kidding!*...

   I wish Jon and his current partner both the best. If they are happy in the relationship...or happy *enough*...well, I hope those two crazy kids make it! They seem to love each other.

   (**If you're Jon's current partner and you're reading this, I'm going to mark RIGHT HERE as where you should STOP reading** I can't tell you what to do, but I can strongly suggest that if you want to live in blissful ignorance, close this book...now!)

   I was happy for him when I learned Jon was in a relationship. I was also glad it wasn't with me. I just hoped he was a nice guy. I met Jon's new partner when Jon and I were still together. I hadn't spent much time around him, but he seemed like a nice guy as far as I could tell. I also hoped Jon would be *different* with Guy, and that they could figure out how to make it work. I remember my sister texting me words of condolence whenever Jon and co. made it 'Facebook official.' I was like, "they've been together for, like, two years...I am not sad about it – he's nice." This also illustrates how little I spoke to *anyone* about the break-up...or the

34

relationship, for that matter. *(But you see what happens when you hold it all in? You end up typing a detailed account of the entire thing to purge yourself of all of it!* **Cuz it's tragedy and it'll only bring you down**...*so you have to set it free!...)*

I also remember one of my earliest trips back to town, when two of our shared friends told me I needed to move back and date Jon again because they weren't big fans of the new boyfriend. I was like, "hell fucking no!" – in my head...what came out of my mouth was more like, "never gonna happen."

When I say I was isolated from the world when living with Jon, these guys were the exception...*kind of.* Their suggestion that Jon and I should make it work was based on what they saw. Jon and I both, for whatever reason, kept them from the full picture. What I mean is, I don't think either of them has ever even smoked meth with Jon...and *that* is rare, especially for inner-circle people... But they would come over to the house most Sundays and swim in the pool, and they'd typically bring friends with them. I had previously been in school with Stuckey and had known him just a bit longer than I'd known Jon. And his husband is great, too! I'd driven into town for their wedding back in 2015. So even though I considered them to be real friends, I understood at that moment that neither of them knew exactly what it was they were encouraging me to walk back into. Because it's not like I talked to *anyone* about 'it' when I was in the middle of it. I didn't have friends I could just call up and chat with about how unhealthy the relationship dynamics were – after all, I felt I needed to protect Jon's **big reputation.** And these were two of Jon's allies...if for no other reason than because Sunday Funday wouldn't be fun without a pool to hang out by. And when I got out, I was not looking back.

It isn't easy to see things for what they are when you're in the middle of them. So I cut ties with the town and its people, many of whom I had been friends with for years - not because of anything they did but because I did not like the person I'd become and because I just needed **blank**

space.   I had no interest in wrecking Jon's perception of his own reputation – I just knew I needed to get away from all of it. And I hoped to reconnect with the person I was *before* Jon – because I <u>really</u> liked him! Jon liked him too…but Jon tends to take things that shine and tarnish them. I don't think it's a conscious plan. It just happens.

I know I'm just a wrinkle in your new life
Staying "friends" would iron it out so nice
………………..
but it's fake and it's oh so unnecessary
      -Closure, Taylor Swift

CHAPTER 15

••••••• ● •••••••

Feedback for an Ex

The first time I started texting Jon with my insights regarding the influence he has on others, I was aboard a cruise ship. It was an all-gay Halloween cruise in 2021, and it was a blast! So there I was, putting money into a slot machine (Jon's lingering influence?) many years after our relationship had ended. Jon and I were texting back and forth, and he was essentially making fun of his current partner (Guy) to me, and it dawned on me: Jon literally has no clue that the things he makes fun of people for are all things that he causes or, at the very least, contributes to... Jon was saying that he'd end things with the dude, but he feels bad because Guy has no skillset and would essentially be destined to fail if he set him free. And so, as Jon found humor in his predicament, I pointed this out to him: Have you ever noticed that when you're dating someone, they tend to become the worst version of themselves? Jon responded that all of his ex's, me included, have gone on to be successful people after him, so he should get some credit for that...

I explained to Jon an alternate perspective – that it was more *because* each of us got away from him that we had an opportunity to thrive. From my perspective, it certainly wasn't that Jon had given me the tools I needed to go out into the world and live my best life once we parted ways. I mean, he is NOT a teacher. Thinking back to any time I went to help him with something at the hotel or at the bar, he'd tell me what he needed done, step away, and then come back when I was half-way done and let me know I'd been doing it wrong...or if he was in a good mood he'd just go behind me and redo whatever it is I'd been doing. So, as far as teaching someone *how* to do something right…he doesn't do that. Quite the opposite. (This can be anything from wiping down a countertop to shampooing a carpet. Hanging up Christmas lights to sanding something that needed to be painted. The thought, "Why am I even here if I can't do anything right?" crossed my mind and factored into me not going to help Jon when he needed it when we were together.)

Anyway, given the situation he currently found himself in, I hoped to open Jon's eyes to the possibility that he was *at least* part of the problem, certainly not the solution.

It's quite shocking to me that Jon could reflect on any of his relationships and think he'd been a *positive* influence. After all, Jon told me about each of his partners and their shortcomings, as well as the substance abuse issues *they'd* developed during the time they were with Jon. This wasn't shared all at once, mind you. Jon would just randomly give tidbits about past boyfriends, harping on how *this* one had become more and more problematic in *this* way…*that* one became increasingly problematic in *that* way…over the time they were with Jon. ["Problematic" is an all-encompassing term, and in this context, I mean some combination of the following: dependent (on substances and/or Jon – often both…), isolated, paranoid/suspicious, *sometimes* angry or resentful, *sometimes* depressed, *often both*. Jon had cheated on *boyfriend x* with whoever was to be *boyfriend y*, in most cases. Other times, he'd simply been a terrible boyfriend in the end. I do not know of a relationship Jon has ended on *good* terms where he wasn't ultimately the one more at fault.

But here he was, talking shit about his current partner as if Jon was doing the dude a solid by keeping him on as a boyfriend, even though he was conveying to me that he didn't want to.

All the boys **that you run dry have tired, lifeless eyes cuz you burned them out**…that's about what it feels like.

CLOSURE

So, in this moment of text message exchanges, I simply wanted Jon to take a minute and spend some time thinking about the role *he* plays in derailing boyfriends – I didn't need an answer or any follow-up. I just wanted him to think over the impact he has on people he dates or otherwise cares about.   And that was that.   I got back to the slot machine aboard the cruise boat, and Jon got back to his boyfriend driving him crazy - walking around the house and trying to play guitar...badly (which was also highlighted during our chat).   Given that Jon was rattling off reasons he wanted to dump the guy, I figured that was where the relationship was headed.   I breathed a sigh of relief, thinking Guy would get out of there sooner rather than later.   Then maybe he'd have a fighting chance at becoming something successful.

[You would think that as the owner of multiple successful businesses throughout his lifetime, and being someone who knew a thing or two about a lot of things, Jon could teach his boyfriend some kind of skill that *was* marketable.   But instead, joking/complaining about his lack of employability was typical of Jon.   (So if you read the last book and wonder why I'd been concerned that Jon would "talk shit" about me back when I was his boyfriend, here was my confirmation that I wasn't just being paranoid.)]

As I mentioned before, I didn't need any follow-up communication about how Jon had or had not taken my words to heart.   After all, I wasn't trying to stir shit up with Jon while I was on vacation!   And I know it's not my 'job' to 'protect' people – Guy or anyone else – from Jon.   But like A.J. before me, I do feel some sense of obligation to help others see the patterns in Jon's relationships so that if the person isn't aware of what's going on, they can hopefully get a clue *before* it blows up in their face.

CHAPTER 16

•••••••• • •••••••

A Summary of His Ex's

~A.J. – A.J. told me directly that he became strung out on cocaine while with Jon. A.J. said that the best thing that ever happened to him was going away to college and getting away from Jon because it got him away from the drugs. A.J. said that had it not been for college, he's not sure he ever would have broken free from Jon. (*A.J. shared the with me after he'd had a couple of cocktails when I was dating Jon, when Jon was maybe 50 feet away, at a bar…I just figured A.J. was a bitter ex-boyfriend who was oversharing at the time.)

~"A." - *all I know about this boyfriend from their time together was that Jon always said, "I was never really attracted to him, physically…" I don't know much more than that about the relationship… "A." is from the town where Jon resides, but he doesn't live there anymore. I think their relationship was short, and I think he was one of the more problematically young guys that Jon dated – at least as far as the boyfriends of years past are concerned – although I'm not certain how young he was when they got together... The dude *is* attractive. (Jon's comments about attraction to this dude always rubbed me the wrong way and felt like an unnecessary thing to include any time Jon brought the dude up.) [*I don't know anything about substance use with this ex of Jon's.]

~Mark – Jon used to say Mark became an alcoholic during the time they were together, referring to him as "a drunk." By Jon's account, Mark had also become "paranoid" – distrustful of Jon, trying to catch Jon when he was up-to-something…Mark was not into drugs, so for Jon to use them, he had to be sneakier. I can't help but speculate that this may've caused/contributed to Mark's paranoia...or maybe it was that...Jon cheated on Mark (or "fell asleep in the pool house" with Rob, I should say...And perhaps he did "fall asleep" that night...but Rob told me they were fucking before they even got together publicly. So 'paranoid' Mark was out, and Rob was in.). [*I did not know Mark personally. We never met or spoke. I just heard about the drama.]

~Rob – Rob stopped dealing meth once he started dating Jon...but he never quit using it. I was a first-hand witness to Rob losing his 'spark' when he lived on Jon's property. He was noticeably less happy, less stable mentally, etc. At the time, I figured this was an internal issue with Rob based on how Jon spun the narrative. I knew nothing of Jon's prior relationships as I watched my best friend change into this less upbeat version of himself, which is why it never dawned on me that Jon was the cause... (*My opinion has since changed.*)

~**Me!** – Jon offered me GHB one day when I was upset. I slept with my best friend's boyfriend, who I hadn't thought of 'like that' previously...meth was made freely available every day for the years that we were together – our morning "coffee," if you will. (For the record, I was not a daily meth user before dating Jon.) Over time, I became the worst version of myself. It wasn't something that happened overnight. But starting a relationship off the way that we had, plus a lot of drug use, plus the way that Jon *is* in a relationship, plus the negative perceptions Jon has of other people...all of this brought me down. Not to mention being cheated on, lied to, and putting up with things in this relationship that I swore I would never put up with...It didn't do wonders for my self-esteem. I didn't have to stay. But what's difficult to put into words fully is that when Jon covertly convinced me that people were envious of my '*situation,*' that people treated his boyfriends "differently," and he'd make fun of the various people in the community who I saw kissing up to him. Somehow, I was tricked into believing I was lucky.

~Guy – Guy is still with Jon. I'm not going to say if Guy is his best self these days…because I didn't know him very well before Jon, so it's not my place. I will say that I include him as part of my evidence that the pattern continues, not because of my observations but because of the things that both he and Jon have told me that support my theories. And for the time being, that's all I'll say about Guy.

CHAPTER 17

· · · · · · · · ● · · · · · · ·

Boxing with No Gloves

The things I most frequently got frustrated with Jon over included the following:

<u>Playing Devil's Advocate</u>: defined as "To argue against or attack an idea, argument, or proposition—even if one is in favor of it—for the sake of debate or to further examine its strength, validity, or details."

Jon used to do this frequently. And he would own it once I was frustrated. "Oh, I was just playing devil's advocate…" It caused multiple incidents where I snapped at him. Jon and I would go back-and-forth-and-back-and-forth, each of us offering up points and counterpoints, clearly on opposing sides of whatever topic we were debating. Sometimes the matter at hand was something impersonal that neither of us had a real connection to, while other times, the topic may be something that came from a first-hand experience or actual, factual knowledge. All too often, what began as a laid-back and friendly conversation suddenly had Jon and myself at odds with one another, typically because Jon had counterpoints and counterarguments for whatever opinion I may offer or factual knowledge I may relay to him, it seemed. We would get to a point in a debate or an argument where I was at my wit's end, asking Jon how he could possibly stand behind the perspective he'd been supporting throughout the conversation we were having, even after I'd offered up what I felt was sufficient evidence to support whatever my stance was. Jon's response in these moments was, inevitably, that he didn't necessarily *feel* aligned with whatever stance he'd been arguing the whole time and that he was merely playing devil's advocate.

In these conversations, locking down how Jon actually felt about anything – from political and social issues to personal things that actually mattered to me – became incredibly irritating. Some of the time, when I'd pose the question of, "but how do you *actually* feel about this topic?" he would say, "I agree with you." (#frustrating – since he'd just spent so much energy arguing-for-the-defense…). Other times, "I don't *actually* really have an opinion on the matter…" (#frustrating – did he just want a spirited debate? Or to ruffle my feathers? Or to be adversarial with me?...I will never know.) **Fighting with him was like trying to solve a crossword and realizing there's no right answer… -Red**, Taylor Swift

Giving unsolicited advice: Basically, having someone offer advice, guidance, suggestions, or their opinion when you have not asked for it. Of course, there are times when you need someone to give you a heads-up before you proceed with stepping on a (metaphorical) land mine. That is simply looking out for someone you care about. That is not what I'm talking about. With Jon, it was more like he'd advise me on how to proceed with something in my life as if I couldn't figure it out on my own. And then, if I followed his suggestion and it blew up in my face or backfired, there was no accountability. But if I *didn't* follow his suggestion, I was met with disappointment and judgment, and it seemed like he was just waiting for the "I told you so" moment. I hadn't asked for advice in the first place, but once the advice had been given, it was too late to get out of what was inevitably going to be a no-win situation for me.

These dynamics were toxic, and we had arguments about "playing devil's advocate" and "giving unsolicited advice" enough times to where, in time, I realized it was just best to avoid letting Jon into my life too much. Because when your partner will pull the devil's advocate card in response to some of his unsolicited advice backfiring on you as if he didn't *mean* for you to follow the advice and he had just been giving the advice from the perspective of a devil's advocate – well, it's then you know that the head games he plays can have major consequences in your life if you don't suss out his motives and his intent in every conversation. And who has time for that? The odds that Jon would just admit that he'd given bad advice without it being a fight were slim to none...with slim being on hiatus. Throughout our relationship, it came to feel more and more like anything I did or said that didn't align with what Jon wanted to have happen was ultimately going to be met with more negative energy than it was worth. So I just came to do and share less and less because it was safer to operate that way.

Jon wasn't physically abusive. But he is excellent at making someone feel very small when they are – from his perspective – wrong. Very, very small.

Jon is who I was dating when I learned one of the hardest things I've learned in this lifetime, and that is that – at least for me – feeling alone and lonely when you are in a relationship with someone feels exponentially worse than feeling alone and lonely as a single person. I felt both isolated and alone for a long time when I was with Jon, even when still living in his house. That was one of the worst places I've ever been, emotionally. And it's a big part of why I'm somewhat relationship-averse today. That and the fact that I don't trust myself to pick a healthy partner.

...cuz it's too late for you and your white horse to come around...

CHAPTER 18

······ • • ······

Gaslighting

Psychologytoday.com says:

How does gaslighting change a victim?

Gaslighting can be psychologically devastating. It violates trust, upends a person's view that people are generally good, and can make them suspicious of everyone close to them. Falling victim to a gaslighter also erodes a person's trust in themselves and makes them forget what they once valued; after all, it's easy to blame themselves for being too trusting, vulnerable, or dependent. The experience may make a victim never want to be part of a relationship again.

The most effective gaslighters are often the hardest to detect; they may be better recognized by their victims' actions and mental state.

Consequences a victim of gaslighting experiences include:

You feel as though you're a much weaker version of yourself, and you were much more strong and confident in the past.

You feel guilty for not feeling happy like you used to.

You've become afraid of "speaking up" or expressing your emotions, so you stay silent instead.

You feel isolated, hopeless, misunderstood, and depressed.

You never quite feel "good enough."

Something is "off" about your partner, but you can't quite explain or pinpoint what.

MedicalNewsToday says:

In relationships, an abusive person may use gaslighting to isolate their partner, undermine their confidence, and make them easier to control.

A person who uses this tactic may have learned it is an effective way of obtaining what they want or controlling people. They may feel entitled to have things their way or that the wants and needs of others do not matter.

- Feeling incompetent, unconfident, or worthless
- Becoming withdrawn or isolated from others

In relationships, gaslighting often begins gradually. The abusive person gains their partner's trust, sometimes with an initial "honeymoon period" in which there is no abusive behavior. Then, the person begins suggesting that their partner is not reliable, that they are forgetful, or that they are mentally unstable.

Examples of types of gaslighting include:

Diverting: With this technique, a person changes the focus of a discussion by questioning the other person's credibility.

Denial: Denial involves a person refusing to take responsibility for their actions.

Trivializing: This occurs when a person belittles or disregards how someone else feels.

Withholding: This involves someone pretending they do not understand the conversation or refusing to listen to make a person doubt themselves.

Countering: This is when someone questions a person's memory.

Hulzen, Jennifer, and Vara Saripalli Psy.D. "What Is Gaslighting?" Medical News Today. Medical News Today, July 14, 2022. https://www.medicalnewstoday.com/articles/gaslighting#how-it-works.

Tactics used by a gaslighter include:

Gaslighters use a variety of subtle techniques to undermine your reality and portray *you* as the disturbed and messed up one.

Discrediting you by making other people think that you're crazy, irrational, or unstable.

Using a mask of confidence, assertiveness, and/or fake compassion to make you believe you "have it all wrong." Therefore, eventually, you begin to doubt yourself and believe *their* version of past events.

Changing the subject. The gaslighter may divert the topic by asking another question or making a statement usually directed at your thoughts.

Minimizing. By trivializing how you feel and what you think, the gaslighter gains more and more power over you, e.g., "Why are you being so sensitive?" "You don't need to get angry over a little thing like that!" "I was just joking around. Why are you taking things so seriously?"

Denial and avoidance. By refusing to acknowledge your feelings and thoughts, the gaslighter causes you to doubt yourself more and more.

Twisting and reframing. When the gaslighter confidently and subtly twists and reframes what was said or done in their favor, they can cause you to second-guess yourself—especially when paired with fake compassion, making you feel as though you are "unstable," "irrational," and so forth.

This is a serious issue that can create long-term harm in your life, especially if you're a sensitive person.

Psychologytoday.com says (in an article titled "Gaslighting," found at

https://www.psychologytoday.com/us/basics/gaslighting): Those who employ this tactic often have a personality disorder, narcissistic personality disorder, and psychopathy chief among them. Manipulators have a tendency to present one face to their prey and another to the rest of the world, leading victims to assume that if they ask for help or speak out, no one will believe that they have been manipulated and emotionally abused. Gaslighters typically repeat the tactics across several relationships.

CHAPTER 19

•••••••• • • •••••••

Long Story Short

Jon let me know Blackie wasn't doing too well and suggested I come for a visit sooner rather than later. I told him sometime earlier in the week that I could be there that weekend, so he offered the pool house so I could spend some time with her. It just so happened to be the weekend of Blackie and Brownie's birthday. So, on March 17th, 2023, I made the trek from Raleigh to Jon's house.

Blackie – one of the chihuahua sisters Jon adopted when we were together – was reportedly close to the end. She's had congestive heart failure for a while now, and when she misses a medication dose, she has a death rattle dry cough that sounds terrible. But she's still a happy dog, and she and her sister Brownie both get very excited when they see me. And while they've softened a bit towards the rest of the world in their old age, they still don't like people, in general. But they love me. And so any time Jon says either of them isn't doing so hot, I will scrap whatever weekend plans I had and come to visit.

Jon was out of town when I went for Blackie's death-rattle visit, and the weekend had been a fun one. I stayed in the pool house. Jon's boyfriend, Guy, lives in the house. For whatever reason, Guy did not go with Jon on whatever trip he was away on. I saw Guy a little bit while I was visiting. He has always been nice to me and hasn't seemed to care that an ex of Jon's is staying on the property.

It's a weird mix of disappointment and relief when I go for a visit, and Jon is not there. Because Jon is still funny and can still make me laugh. And sometimes, I'm not bothered by the things about him that drove me nuts when he was my boyfriend. *Sometimes.*

There was a time after our break-up when I could visit and get along well with Jon. But I'm beginning to think those days are a thing of the past. Because even though I've gotten away from the situation and try not to look back, the pattern continues. It's a pattern that I feel stupid now for falling into at 23. I didn't get out until I was 30. I stuck it out past the age of most. Mark left Jon and landed on Jon's ex-list when he was 33. Rob was 25 when they broke up, I think...A.J. was younger than any of us, I'm assuming, since he left Jon to start college..."A." was from Jon's town, so I'm uncertain how old he was when they got together... But of the people whose ages I can approximate when they started dating Jon: Rob was 23 to Jon's 45, I was 23 to Jon's 47, Guy was 21 to Jon's 54 (about). (*A wise woman once sang, **I get older, but your lovers stay my age...**). Guy is currently 28, to Jon's 61. (**Tick-tock on the clock...?**)

And speaking of ex's...remember mine?

Kris and Kris's boyfriend, Jacob, also live on Jon's property in the detached apartment over the garage. They've lived there for at least a few years now. As sad as it is to report, Kris doesn't make much dance magic anymore...not regularly, anyway. I'd have to imagine dancing is hard on your body, so I guess being a choreographer isn't something you can do forever. Admittedly, I'm speculating about that – I just know my body hurts in ways it didn't a decade ago, and my dancing is just the club-kind, no skill involved. He was – and I'm sure still is – a ridiculously talented choreographer.

CHAPTER 20

······ • • ● • • ·······

The Queens Nemesis has a Song About *This...*

To the tune of Fallout Boy's "This Aint A Scene, It's An Arms Race," I'd like to lead with:

"This ain't a brag. It's a goddamn expla-nation…" I am incredibly fortunate: My undergrad experience was paid for by my parents, and grad school was fully funded by my mother. And I've been blessed to not have to deal with student loan debt because of this. I always had a car when I was in college and grad school, which was paid for. I paid for car insurance myself, but that was it. Sometime after I graduated from college and the transmission on my Acura SUV blew, I began driving a blue Volkswagen Passat.

For most of my 20's I had two jobs at a time – typically one job working at a hotel, the other working in mental health. Sometimes, these were both full-time positions, but most of the time, only one of the two jobs was full-time (usually the one in mental health since that was my intended career path.) I am spelling out things related to my finances because I didn't want anyone to think I was with Jon because I'm a "gold digger." People used to pose such questions about other boyfriends Jon had been with, and while no one has ever said anything like that to my face, it crossed my mind that someone somewhere could be thinking that's why I was in this relationship. It is not. I had my own money from working, access to a sizeable investment account that my parents had started long ago, and savings. *It is not lost on me the value of graduating from school without student loan debt. [**<u>Privilege is real</u>. People who *still* say otherwise? Well, unfortunately, ignorance is <u>also</u> very real.] So, while it was cool not to have to pay rent while living with Jon, the financial piece didn't really factor into me getting with him, staying with him, or leaving. (**In summary: this chapter is an excellent example of KW's words proving once again to be <u>completely irrelevant</u>.*)

I worked the front desk at Jon's hotel before he and I dated...when we were friends...when we were dodging Rob...and on through 'til we were officially boyfriends. This means I knew all of my colleagues at the hotel before it was common knowledge that I had any connection to Jon. He did not help me to get the job and I did not get paid any more than anyone else working at the front desk. Nor should I – I just want it to be clear there were no special favors connected to my employment at his hotel.

Everyone working at Jon's hotel shared another commonality: He didn't compliment any of us, no matter how hard we worked. He was on the property pretty regularly and would hear from the manager about the positive reviews individuals would get on Trip Advisor, how hard the housekeepers had worked to get a suite ready for a guest who had arrived early, or how the conference center's manager had gone above-and-beyond to make a wedding reception run smoothly. The most meaningful sentiment Jon *might* express to someone would be something along the lines of *Keep it up,* although often he didn't acknowledge the employee's hard work to their faces, instead just telling the manager he was glad to hear people were doing their jobs. But don't get it twisted! The employees all *liked* him! He was friendly to everyone – just not the type to congratulate, applaud, thank, or otherwise show appreciation (verbally).

Even after I became his boyfriend, I never heard a complimentary word from him during my work day. I wasn't appreciated more than any housekeeper, maintenance man, manager, or other front desk person. So, in that way, Jon truly was an equal-opportunity kind of guy. I guess if he showed one employee a little appreciation, maybe we'd all be left wondering why he was playing favorites? I'm not sure...but like I said, I wasn't treated any better by him than anyone else who worked for him. *To be clear: I was okay with not being treated *better*. I just feel like we all should have been appreciated for all the money we made him.... (*this is where Rob might interject that I sound like I'm "bitter-dot-com," lol. He always made me laugh.)

CHAPTER 21

· · · · · · · · ● · ● · · · · · · ·

Let's Talk Love Languages

It is entirely possible that this was not as bothersome to other hotel employees as it was to me, and that most of why I'm even bringing it up is not because I'm still irritated that my former boss was unable to show appreciation, but more because I dated the dude and this was not just a mask he wore as the hotel owner. But let's look at it from the languages-of-love perspective. At any front desk hotel job I've had, the point is made regularly that the people working at the front desk are the first employees with an opportunity to make a good impression on guests. I've always gotten feedback that I'm very helpful, bubbly, and that guests love me. That sounds like a brag, but it's just my personality. (I *used to* suffer from REALLY high self-esteem...*that was sarcasm.) Front desk personnel are programmed to thrive on *words of affirmation*. If a guest named an individual in a Trip Advisor review for going above and beyond, that person got $20 as an incentive to keep up the good work. And fortunately, the hotel's general manager regularly offered *words of affirmation* to people in all departments of the hotel. She did what she could to make up for what Jon was not programmed to do, so it was a good thing he hired her - she was an awesome manager and a great 'people person.'

For anyone whose love language is *gifts*, I suppose the argument could be made that the incentives program came with a *gift* to those who performed *acts of service* for our guests, and the whole lack-of-compliments observation is simply me making an issue out of nothing. But for the hotel owner (Jon) - who was often at the hotel doing construction projects

- I don't think it would have killed him to tell someone…anyone…that they were doing a great job. Instead, his presence at the hotel was unsettling for all employees, as he was ever-ready to offer up criticism. We would 'batten down the hatches' when his work SUV would turn into the parking lot – with the quickness. Everyone would suddenly spring into action, dusting things that had no dust on them or rearranging the snacks in the snack shop – alphabetically this time, rather than by category – to give the illusion of busyness. Because otherwise, quizmaster Jon would want to know *why* we weren't doing *something* in our 'downtime' before guests arrived. Rest assured, Jon set a very consistent tone just by being himself: none of us ever felt *special* (/appreciated…) by him. Not through *words of affirmation,* anyway.

The brown-nosing front desk manager inquired *at* Jon as Jon breezed through the lobby one day, "Did you happen to see Jon? Four different guests have mentioned me, by name, for exemplary service on TripAdvisor in the past couple of weeks!" Jon's response? "Glad to hear you're doing what's expected of you…maybe in the next couple of weeks try and shoot for six…". (*that is the secondhand retelling of a story that, admittedly, I was not present for. When Jon initially told me about this exchange, I thought it was funny because I was not a big fan of my manager at the front desk. Jon was not a fan, either. But not long after tooting his own horn, the front desk manager asked for a raise. Jon told me, at home, that he respected this guy for being such a strong self-promoter because even if he didn't like the guy, it took guts to make the request so directly. Jon noted that he didn't become successful as a business owner by going out of his way to pay employees more than he had to, so while he'd never been one to <u>offer</u> anyone a raise, this guy demanding to be paid what he felt he was worth struck a chord with Jon. And he got a raise.*)

When Jon wasn't driving his work SUV (my former Acura, with its new transmission, and now filled with Jon's power tools), he, too, had a VW Passat. The only difference was that his was black. When we got together, we each already had our respective cars. I drove to work at the hotel each day in my Passat. Jon sometimes came in the SUV but occasionally came in his Passat. So even though our choice of make and model was purely coincidental, it didn't stop gossipy people from gossiping...

Not long after the cat was out-of-the-bag that Jon and I were dating, I came in for my shift at the hotel front desk. That's when co-worker Melinda shared (about our front desk manager): "Do you know what Jimbo said? He said "I'll-bet-you-anything-Jon-bought-Bruce-his-car..."..."

Umm...(it would've been a sweet thing to do...but) <u>No-the-fuck-he-didn't!</u>

Admittedly, it is 100% believable that Melinda may've totally concocted this story on her own, given that she was the reigning queen of stirring shit up amongst EVERYBODY at the hotel (and I knew this...). But Jimbo's "alleged" suggestion that Jon had bought me a car was ridiculous. I relayed this story to Jon, and he just reminded me: See-what-I-said? People-just-treat-you-*different* – my-boyfriends-have-*always*-said-that...

What does this have to do with Love Languages, you may be asking?? And for others who are thinking, "What is a love language??" Here is my attempt at the Cliff's Notes summary - *note: I have not read the book that introduced the concept of love languages, so I may butcher this... **Let's see how I do...**

The 5 'languages' are:

Touch – this includes anything from touching your partner's shoulder to show affection, to giving a massage, to sex (and I guess to add a modern spin: we're talking <u>consensual</u> touch – which *can* include kinks that involve touch – IF your partner experiences that as love, or if you do – no shame. Love is love. Different strokes for different folks!...(just make sure all stroking is consensual.)

Gifts – If Jimbo was right and Jon had bought me a car, that would've been one helluva Gift. But gifts don't have to be expensive. Gifts are always worth exploring in therapy when working with couples because some people get so much joy out of GIVING a thoughtful, personal gift to someone they love but HATE getting gifts. Other times, one partner – partner #1 – may give their significant other – partner #2 – pricey items for birthdays and anniversaries, but then get irritated when those items aren't treated well or partner #2 doesn't also give a similarly priced gift. Without intervention, partner #1 may become resentful over time.

Meanwhile, partner #2 probably doesn't receive gifts as love – it just IS NOT their love language. It's not their fault – it's just something worth knowing about your partner before the resentment builds. Finally, there are people who would prefer a handmade gift over an expensive one any day – useful information if you're about to surprise someone with a gift you could barely afford!

Words of Affirmation - **...and he says, "You look beautiful tonight..." and I feel perfectly *fine*...** Words of affirmation can be "You look sexy as fuck in that spandex" or "Thanks for picking up the kids. It was a big help." "You're the most beautiful woman in the room..." or "I love you." For some, they come naturally. For others, not so much. There are some caveats worth noting as they relate to words of affirmation. For example, if your partner has low self-esteem and constantly needs reassurance that you love them, you appreciate them, and you promise you'll never leave them – and if you don't tell them often *enough*...well, your partner may need therapy. Words of affirmation can be so incredibly powerful towards someone feeling loved. "I realize I don't say it as much as I should, but you do so much around this house, and you are literally the only reason this family functions. Keeping up with everyone's schedule? Reminding me to take my meds...keeping this place as clean as the kids will allow it to be. I am so grateful that I get to do *this* – all of it – with *you* as my partner!" If words of affirmation register as a love language for the partner hearing these words, great! But if words of affirmation are not in the partner's top 2, you may be better off *showing* rather than *telling*, with an...

Act(s) of Service – example: I noticed the emergency light was on in your car, so I brought it in for an oil change because I know how much you hate going and doing it...and now it's done! *(yay!). // Planning a date night...especially if you're not typically 'the planner' in the relationship and your partner has been overwhelmed lately. This may entail booking a sitter, making reservations, and even picking a movie you know your partner has wanted to see. Or cleaning up the house when your wife is coming back from a business trip, and you know she'll be happier to be home if she doesn't have to 'tackle the kitchen' when she gets there. Acts of service, I believe, are generally things you think to do for your significant other's benefit, just because you were thinking of them and wanted to make their life a bit easier, so you did *it*, whatever 'it' was...

Time – I tend to speak about the concept of time as two separate ideas – those two ideas being quality time and quantity time. Some people feel loved simply by being in the same space as their partner, even if there's not a lot of interaction. If a person loves quantity time, they may just want to watch TV while their partner reads, and they may feel loved and comforted by their partner's presence. On the flip side, quality time is time carved out for connection. One-on-one date nights with your partner, where a pair can catch up or reconnect without distractions, devices, kids, etc, is quality time.

Love languages are not unique to romantic relationships. As a therapist, I have had clients with divorced parents who know when their parent is attempting to show love by giving expensive gifts when what the kid really wants is quality time with the parent. If your kid's love language is not gifts, continuing to buy them, things may be making them angrier rather than rebuilding a bridge.

I have found that most people are able to identify at least one but often two of these as their preferred love languages once they have all of the information. **It is NOT necessary to have the same or even similar love languages as your partner!** It can be incredibly helpful to know and understand your partner's love language(s) as well as your own. Because not knowing this information can leave you feeling really stuck. Knowing which of these don't register with your partner is just as important. If emptying the dishwasher (act of service) means more to your partner than buying expensive gifts, you can waste a lot of money and never accomplish your goal of letting your partner know how much you love them.

Something I've seen numerous times is a relationship where one partner is asking for more touch (specifically, sex), and their partner is not in the mood. The partner who is not in the mood may have any number of things going on, but often, it's about being exhausted, overwhelmed, and feeling like most of the *things* fall on them (household cleaning, getting the kids where they need to be, etc.). It is amazing how acts of service can turn this dynamic around! If you are the partner wanting more physical affection, quit asking for it and instead DO something kind for your partner that is unexpected and that lessens the degree to which they feel burdened. If your partner is constantly *too tired* to have sex, what can you do to make your partner's life easier each day, thereby freeing up some of their energy? *Doing* those things will generally help your partner to be more attracted to the idea of having sex. Plus, asking for sex when your partner isn't in the mood can feel like a rejection, and when sex begins to take on more of a negative connotation in a relationship, it can become very problematic. Avoid nagging, complaining, or bringing guilt into the equation when the topic of sex is on the table. Unless you don't want to have it anymore, in which case all of those things will help you to achieve that goal.]

CHAPTER 22

•••••••• • •••••••

This is why we can't have nice things

Fortunately, when dating Jon, I never experienced too much of a shift in how most people treated me. But for a while, I did find myself wondering when this shift was going to happen and hoping that it wouldn't. After all, I was well-liked in my college town...I had a lot of great friends in the gay community there. I was regularly out at the club. I had a tendency to meet new people everywhere I went. I also had plenty of straight friends, many of whom I'd go to Jon's nightclub with before he and I dated because who doesn't have time for a drag show?? But more often, I'd go to straight bars with these friends (because I liked the music at straight bars better at that time). Not to mention, there was a lot more of a variety of straight bars and clubs downtown. All of this provided me with insight into where to send guests at the hotel, who would ask on weekends, "Hey, where's a good dive bar?" or "Where can I get the best mojito downtown?" And while Jon and I did do *some* bouncing around to see what other clubs were like on the weekends, once we were dating, this happened less and less frequently.

I'm not suggesting I was 'held prisoner' or anything, but I certainly wasn't going to grab a gay friend of mine from his club and head to a straight bar without Jon! I knew better! I got a lot of hell for moves I made and for having fun, specifically, if it ever involved another guy and Jon wasn't present to witness what-the-fuck had gone on...and he certainly wasn't going to take my word for it. Being friendly – which is and always has been my natural disposition - tended to get me in trouble once Jon and I started dating. I could be friendly towards people Jon knew I wasn't attracted to. But attractive guys, including ones I'd been friends with before Jon and I dated, no. This was a double standard in our relationship, as Jon was allowed to befriend attractive guys. Some he'd be obviously interested in, others he'd invite home without consulting me first when I wasn't even sure when he'd made the arrangements or what the expectations were until Jon told me as though I should have gotten the info telepathically. If I thought someone was cute and voiced it to Jon, the person was inevitably unattractive in his eyes, even if objectively they were attractive. Or if the person came up to me at the club and started flirting and blatantly said they wanted to hook up with us both, that person was unattractive in Jon's eyes. Sometimes, we'd take the person home, and Jon would let me know either during or after that he had never been into the guy, as if he was doing me a favor. But he never said it ahead of time, even when given every opportunity to, just afterwards (Jon perpetuated a 'wrong feeling' in the relationship, which is the best way I can put it). And I ALWAYS communicated with Jon up-front, like, "Hey, this dude wants to come home with us...what do you think?" And I always made it clear I'd tell the dude "no" if that's what Jon wanted. (*I'm using absolutes here because I talked to Jon ahead of time, every time. It would have NEVER been acceptable if there was a random guy trailing us to the car or on our walk home, and when Jon said, "Who's he?" I said, "Oh, that's Randy...he's coming home with us because he wants to fuck you. Randy, this is Jon...Jon, Randy." And yet, Jon did this to me. Multiple times. Even after I'd made it clear: You MUST talk to me FIRST.) With Jon, I regularly felt like the last to know, kinda like Jon had inside jokes with dudes who were closer to my age. I never brought this up to Jon, as I didn't see the point. He didn't get the concept of consent, and I was certain his default would be to try to make

61

me question my sanity, so it just wasn't worth it. There was a power dynamic. There were double standards. I saw it with Rob. I experienced it first-hand. Now, you'd have to ask Guy if Jon has evolved…

Generally, Jon has dated guys that go into the relationship less friendly than I am in the time that I've known him…and they've come out much less friendly than they were going in. I include myself as someone who came out much less friendly than I went in. I am stating this as an observation, not trying to throw shade at other partners.

I had watched Rob stick by Jon's side really badly any time they were out at the club when they were dating, and it drove me nuts. I don't ever remember Jon expressing he was irritated by Rob's latching onto him…but I knew when I was dating Jon, this would not be me. I ran around the club and had fun, and I felt like just because Jon needed to be on the 3rd floor doing owner-related activities, it didn't mean I had to be. And when Jon would come down and be 'amongst the people,' I was always excited he'd graced us with THAT FACE! I loved when he'd play pool with me. I'd make slutty wagers that the winner would have to collect when we got home. There was a time when I truly found him to be more loveable than frustrating. I couldn't tell you which months or during what years I felt that way now, but I know those days existed. Back then, I still had good self-esteem. He was more fun and friendly than avoidant or belittling…During that scrumpett of time, I loved him.

There's a level of optimism and naivete that I lost forever during the time I dated Jon. If only it was possible, I'd like to rediscover that way of being, that way of thinking. And if I ever recaptured it, I would not let anyone take it away. I'd avoid anyone spending any significant amount of time around anyone who didn't inspire me to be a **better man** because **I see the permanent damage you did to me. Never again…**I would protect the hell out of my **innocence** so much better if I had the chance to do it all over again. To

have back what was lost during that relationship…man! I'd
kill   for   a   do-over.

CHAPTER 23

•••••••• • •••••••

You're Not Sorry

I used to shine so bright, but I watched all of it fade... What Jon liked best about me initially, he also extinguished. It may be weird to say that, but it's clear to me now that is what happened. He used to even say it himself! That I seemed different, that I wasn't happy like I used to be, that I avoided him...Again, I don't think he's an *intentional* 'spirit-killer.' I just think he hasn't spent the time in self-reflection that would be necessary for him to see it. I wasn't the first person whose spirit died on his property, and sadly, I do not anticipate mine will be the last.

I can tell you my perspective on *what* happened, but so much of *why* he did what he did or behaved the way he did is something only he can explain. Including his emails provide some insight into what he was thinking, but many of his *actual* motives I will never know for sure...

My own experiences with Jon, especially the ones I found to be most painful to go through or the ones where he can easily be seen as the bad guy, I can look at through a 'best case' lens and a 'worst case' lens. Like, best case, Jon offered me GHB because I was sad the first day we had sex because he thought that would be a mood booster. Worst case? Jon is a **mastermind** who wanted to be done with Rob once and for all, so he saw his chance to lock down his exit strategy by giving GHB to Rob's best friend, thereby making someone else complicit in the break-up. After all, it was the first time Jon had offered me GHB when it was just the two of us, but not the first time I'd been by the house and seen Jon when

Rob was at work. So why this time? It really just depends on how calculating Jon actually is in his own mind. Best case = he's blissfully ignorant, worst case = he's a calculated narcissist. My hope is that someone will read both this book and **Better Man** and give me a final answer.

No one made me stay with him. My friends and family would have intervened if they'd found out about the drugs and stuff. So maybe *that's* why I put space between myself and the outside world – because I didn't *want* anyone busting up my dysfunctional 'chosen' family...?

In so many ways, I became so disconnected from myself during my years with Jon that figuring out what kept me in the relationship is something I can't make complete sense of myself. **...sometimes I wonder how you think about it now...?** But here I am, writing out how I think about it now...And doing my best to document this **illicit affair** as thoroughly as I can.

Don't call me kid, don't call me baby, look at this idiotic fool that you made me...
And you know damn well, for you I would ruin myself, a million little times...
       -Illicit affairs, Taylor Swift

CHAPTER 24

•••••••• • •••••••

Blind optimism to blame...?

I have tried to give everyone I meet the benefit of the doubt. I like forming my own impression of a person, and when someone tells me someone is 'bad news,' I inevitably have to see for myself. And it's easily the part of the 'moral code' I operate by that has bitten me in the ass the most frequently and the hardest.

I look back in regret, I ignored when they said "run as fast as you can...."
-**Dear Jo(h)n** -Taylor Swift.

But **maybe it's me and my blind optimism to blame...** The crappy thing is it's that blind optimism that I haven't been able to recover since leaving Jon. I like myself a lot more, that's for sure - not having someone who's **never impressed by me acing your tests** helps. I'm not sure how long Taylor was with Mr. Mayer, but if she could multiply her experience out to where it had been a six-year ordeal...and throw in meth addiction...and then watch him keep repeating his pattern with other people, both a romantic partner and with people who are my friends...well, I'd like to think Taylor would have written a book, too. (*I'm sure it would be much more cohesive and lovely, and sell billions of copies. Which is why I love her.)

I was raised in a world where older people consistently looked out for me and wanted to guide me in the right direction. Teachers, youth group leaders, immediate and extended family members, parents of friends...really, all adults. Generally, there was a sense that if someone was my elder, they were not going to steer me in the wrong direction. I realize now that this is not everyone's childhood experience and that I'm speaking from a place of privilege. But it never occurred to me that someone who was twice my age might not actually have my best interest at heart...or, more accurately, in mind. Considering the impact he may be having on my life, both in the immediate sense and long-term, was probably not something Jon was regularly reflecting upon. Although my younger self kind of just assumed that because he was older, his intentions would surely equal out to a net positive...right? I learned a hard lesson - that, no, that is not a thing. But maybe that's not a character defect in Jon. It's just a different mindset and a different way of navigating the world than I have.

What made Jon so interesting to me in my early 20's was him thinking about things in such a different way than I do. I've seen him navigate through a situation that ultimately did not work out the way he had planned, but then have no regrets about how he handled things. I've seen him backed into a corner with undeniable evidence of something he'd done but still make it someone else's fault or evade taking responsibility. And I've seen him behave like a jackass plenty of times, but I've never _heard_ him apologize (although he has typed "sorry" in emails...and to be fair, one of these times was an actual apology, it just came with a number of paragraphs about why he thought his behavior was okay, in the moment). I've seen him become offended by someone doing something to him, even if it's the exact behavior I've seen him do to someone else. What I'm really trying to say here is simply this: No matter how interesting his perspective on something may be or how fascinated I may be by how differently his brain works, in retrospect, Jon was a **bad idea**.

CHAPTER 25

· · · · · · · ● · · · · · · · ·

To All the Jon's of the world:

~No one should encourage their partner to be more jaded…(why not let this happen naturally – it's such a terrible thing to rush!).

~Don't encourage your partner to see ulterior motives in people if you aren't certain the person actually has ulterior motives (for being kind and other such behavior that you find suspicious). *Plenty of people ARE NICE! If you're nice to them, they're nice to you…

~Don't insist that people who don't steal a little are stealing a lot. (I know this is a joke you say and a line from a movie, but kind of like your, "If you don't have anything nice to say, come sit by me", you do mean it.)

~Stop getting young dudes addicted to drugs so that you have a boyfriend.

Ask yourself: If you didn't have **nice things**, would people stick around because you're a nice person..?..?…. (something everyone could benefit from thinking about and adjusting their behavior accordingly).

It's hard to live in a world where you don't know if anyone likes you or if they're just there for the afterparty…

I knew everyone liked me before I was with Jon. After Jon, I didn't even like me. Unfortunately, Jon's way of thinking inevitably rubs off on his partner's.

CHAPTER 26

•••••••• • ••••••••

Enemies with an Ex?

Anyone I've ever dated, I'd be happy to help out, if they needed it. And if I ran into them somewhere or saw them in a grocery store, I'd go out of my way to say "hello." Well...except for one of them. Nathan. Because helping him – which he used to rope me into doing regularly after we'd broken up – always comes with strings. And he can only rock that superficial charm for a very short time before all the symptoms of a disordered personality shine through once again. And he's mean, and he's a victim, and it's all my fault again. All my fault because, according to him, he fell so deeply in love with me that the fact that we aren't together anymore – and the fact that I dumped him because he cannot tell the truth – the fact that I put *him* through *that,* has ruined him. Permanently. According to him.

PS – if someone you dated for a month and a half, many years ago, reaches out because he needs the advice of someone he trusts...but then he never tells you what advice is needed...or if he attempts to convince you that you're the reason he can't get a job or find **happiness**...and he lies compulsively...And yet, even knowing all of these and many additional defects of character, you still wonder if he's okay once in a while, and you're embarrassed to admit you still worry about him...well, then you also dated someone with BPD. And if you set boundaries and y'all are not in contact anymore...you're doing good. It's what is best for BOTH of you – remember how you ruined his life?! Yes, self. I remember. Okay, good talk...

CLOSURE

*Suggested listen: **I did something bad...** -Taylor Swift

The further I am from my last thought of Nathan, the happier I am. There's only so many times his predictable lines can work before I'm simply an idiot if I invite that back into my life. I'd like to shed light on what is and what is not a level of anger and hostility to see in your partner or some insight into how to effectively get someone with rage issues into therapy, but I failed to figure that out with Nathan. I just learned last weekend that he's back in jail, and that tends to have an overall positive impact on his mental health, even if only temporarily. In the past, he has gotten medication and therapy when he's incarcerated, and if he ever sticks with it after he's released, who knows what he could do with his life?

Final thought: If you're dating someone who you've realized is incredibly manipulative. Then you let them know they're "manipulative," and they proceed to use their emotional hurt over being assaulted with such a hateful word as leverage...and then they want some form of apology or a romantic gesture if you expect to ever receive their forgiveness...and if you don't fight for that forgiveness they're going to make your life into an awake-nightmare of emotionally dysregulated torture...well... you're probably dating Nathan.

My best suggestion is that you disappear quietly in the night. Because if you are dating Nathan...or someone *like* Nathan, then you've seen how vindictive he can be towards people who, just last week, were some of his "best friends." So, disappearing in the night and never resurfacing may convince him you were kidnapped and hopefully won't trigger his abandonment issues. And if you can successfully get out, just run, girl! Run!!

*Suggested listen: **Now That We Don't Talk,** -Taylor Swift

CHAPTER 27

•••••••• • ••••••••

XXX

Jon and I recorded a lot of sex videos during the time we were together. So much so that, when we'd been together for four years, I burned a two-disc compilation video. "4 years of sex..." Parts 1 and part 2. Part 1 was the sexiest clips edited together – nothing but hardcore action **for just us to know.** But the part 2 disc was more just what was left over - too good to just let disappear into oblivion, but at the same time <u>not</u> guaranteed to be sexy. These DVD discs stayed locked in a lockbox of mine in Raleigh for at least five years after Jon and I broke up, collecting dust. Then finally, I decided that – why not? – I may as well check them out to see if I was any good at video editing (...I needed no proof that I'm dynamite in bed, lol). And while the first disc was not particularly entertaining (...it turns out watching sex of you with an ex is just not as hot as it was when y'all were together...), disc 2 proved to be a <u>real</u> gem! Because it reminded me how much we laughed together and how funny we were. Some highlights include the following lighthearted exchanges:

{On May 1st of 2011, the scene opens like this...}

Jon and I were in our bedroom, having sex...then we stopped. There's a lot of chatter back and forth. Lighting gets adjusted. Sex positions change up. All-the-while, Jon and I are joking back and forth...Jon asks, "Don't we have a detached camera? Didn't you get a webcam? Can you turn your computer on and hook up the detached camera? I want you to <u>see</u> what's going on *in* your <u>asshole</u>." *He always was so thoughtful ...Then he started joking, "I wanna go get a

Cup Cake…Seriously, I'm hungry for a Cup Cake." Then he started singing, "I feel like the Cup Cake is my bodyguard…" (to the tune of Kelly Rowland's "Bodyguard.") [Note to readers: this is what GHB looks like as a bedroom drug.]

Me: "Hey…remember that time you had a muffin face, and I kissed it off??"

Jon continued to struggle with setting up a laptop computer camera and was getting stuck. He had to download or update software…something was wrong. He wasn't getting anywhere…Then it became a team effort – a riddle we were both trying to solve…for 5 or so minutes. Then…

Me: "And *what* is that? It's YOUR FACE…and…it's…wait for it…wait for it….ADORABLE!"

This clip from our bedroom featured me going off on a monologue about how adorable Jon's face is. Meanwhile, the entire time, Jon is working on getting one laptop's camera to work properly while another laptop is recording the video of Jon doing so. Jon is clearly reacting to each ridiculous thing I say, rolling his eyes and looking concerned that he's dating a nonsensical goofball, as I just keep accusing him of operating with too-high-a-level-of-adorability, all the time. He is smiling the whole time, but you can tell he's thinking that I am ridiculous. Jon insists he needs the camera to record our sexual encounter "for posterity," noting that someday when he gathers his grandkids around to watch our porn video, he wants to be sure he's fully captured his "little dumpett scrumpett" in a way that the grandkids can appreciate.

All I have to say about that is, "Look at your face!......it…..is……adorable!"

Our next video was from Jon's office, where he had set up the sling. And he was in it! I was fucking him for a lonnnggg time, (with my penis…then with a tremendous glass dildo Jon made with the blow torch I got him for his birthday one year…then my penis again.) I cum. Then I walk off-camera, which was shooting from overhead. Jon looks over his shoulder at me and says, "You're just a little baby man

man baby…" Hearing the ridiculously stupid words that I said to him all the time come out of his mouth all these years later made me laugh so hard. And hearing Jon sing about his "achy breaky hole" while laid up in a sling – it just felt like comedy gold.

Finally, an additional clip was shot in the pool house in January of 2013. The sling from the last video in Jon's office made it out to the 2nd floor of the pool house for this video shoot. And while whatever laptop we were using had been poorly positioned for a lot of this very lengthy video, the audio is captured…and it is hilarious.

"It's gonna hurt me more than it's gonna hurt you…" was a line Jon used to drop frequently, with this moment in time being no different. *Then*…(Me, *shrieking*.) "Take that cock…That's it..Yeah…take it like a little rockabilly bitch…" (moaning) "Get that thing…get a little motion-of-the-ocean going…huh!…" was his next comment. We're switching up positions, but doing our best to keep his dick in me, and he says, "Would ya look at that." I say "Oop, yeah" (Jon laughs…) "What, you don't need *that* ball..?" I ask. Then I say, "Ew, shit, I feel it movin'…" Jon says, "That's just *them* snappin'…and poppin'…poppin' balls. Don't worry about it." "Jonny McChipples!" I say. "Ow..oh o o.

I must've wiggled the wrong way because we both let out exasperated noises in a panic, and then Jon exclaims, "Oh my God! I can't believe that just happened…"

"No, but I can put it back in. It can go back in…."

"Well, then put it back in!…."

"I got it back in!…"

"…little bitch…put it back in there, you can put it in there like a good little bitch…"

"why are you…saying that word…?…"

"cuz, that's my *word* today, bitch!"

"Shut up…"

"What?"

"Just stop talkin'…"

"I'm not talkin…" …

"oh fuck!..." I shriek.

Jon says: "Come on…come on…it just snaps into the hole…just let it snap into the hole…"

Me: "I'm not coordinated enough for this shit…" "Oh fuck! There it goes!" (moaning)…(shriek/moaning…)

Jon: "Come on, lift your legs, lift your legs…*Now* we're talking with gas…"

Me: "Talking with gas?..."

Jon: "Fuckin' with it…cookin'…cookin' with it…" Me: "*That's* more like it!..."

[…We are changing positions…]

Jon: "…cookin' with the gas…My penis, I don't think it's big enough for *this*…"

Me: "I know, I don't either…"

Jon: "Oh! Well…great! Now you said I have a small cock…"

Me: "well, no, I was just thinkin' it..I was thinkin' it then, but now I'm *sayin'* it…."

Jon: "…and now you're sayin' I've got a teeny dick."

Me: "no…shhh"

Jon: "Call me Mouse Dick [Jon] Carter…Old Carter-the-mouse-dick…."

Me: "mouse dick…no!…mice don't have dicks *that* fat…"

(pause….mumbling….then:)

Jon: "whoa whoa whoa! Brucey!...that's my penis floppin' in and out of your hole…"

Me. "oh….fuck fuck fuck…ah!….oh fuck…." (it goes on from there, back into sex for a while)

The funny thing about most of this 'video' is it's at an angle that you don't see all that much of what's happening. And it had me cracking up!! I knew I had to text Jon, letting him know about the gay comic duo I'd stumbled upon. I had given Jon a heads-up about the "part 2" video and how funny it was once before, but this second time viewing it, I felt like I really needed to watch it – with him. Not for the sexual aspect, but just because it is so fucking funny. And so I sent

CLOSURE

Jon a text message, stating, "I may have already had this conversation with you, but do you know that you and I are sex comedians?" Rather than wait for his reply, I called him to explain what the hell I was talking about. And so, he invited me to bring myself and the videos, and we'd see just how funny it was together...

CHAPTER 28

•••••• • • •••••

Another Funny Exchange

Jon and I are on video, taking a very short break from having sling sex in the pool house, discussing what's next on the agenda.   Apparently, there was a dildo – I think a "Rabbit" sex toy - out there with us. Jon mentioned how *some people* can just take a dildo like that, no problem. Jon makes the comment, "I'm gonna put <u>this</u> in there, and my dick." (*Double penetration was not a 'thing' for me…)

I say, "Mmm, not, like, both…but we'll see...*maybe*…" I go to lay back in the sling, and he picks up the toy and walks over. (Yikes!)

I say, "No, no, no! I said *maybe*…that doesn't mean grab it!..." (laughing)

Jon: "…my god…" (eyeroll)   "…We'll try it!…"

I'm clearly nervous… "Whoa whoa whoa!…Jon, your dick is plenty fat…Why would you want a hole after it's all stretched out? Hot-dog-in-a-hallway! Why are you tryin' to go for that? Why are you goin' for that?........Why you trying to make *me* a hallway..?.." (laughs)

(Bullet dodged. Thank god!)

A bit more talking about his dick…"My d-ock…you want this d-ock? *This* dick!?..." (*We had recently watched Wanderlust – the Paul Rudd mirror scene is epic…)

A minute later, he's letting me know, "I'm gonna cum so hard it's gonna come out your mouth."

He is so funny, so ridiculous, and so 'wide-open' in these videos. And so am I…(after all, I'm the one in the sling…lol)

76

CLOSURE

A good bit of the exercise and endorphins that came from sex with Jon were from laughing so damn much. Jon was hilarious. He still can be, even with clothes on. But he's much funnier in these videos. We would fuck for hours and hours. When we were having sex, **we were happy.**

In one of the videos from 2011, I make a joke about that-<u>one</u>-time-we-*didn't*-have-sex..?...lol.

CHAPTER 29

•••••••• • ••••••

The Eras Tour!....Movie!

On September 1ˢᵗ, 2023, at 1:50 AM, I sent my best friend, Britt, the trailer to **Taylor Swift: The Eras Tour** movie, followed by this text message…

"I just know that if I had sent her fan mail when I first fell in love with her, we'd be in a best friendship throuple (thrupple? Apparently I can't spell or Apple is behind the times…? I got red underlines on both)

Anyway, even if Taylor isn't in our puddle of love, I love you and I wanted you to know that.

Smooches ☺"

Britt wrote back at 8:32 AM…

"…I cannot WAIT for that movie to be released on streaming so I can QUEEN OUT dancing and singing at home!!! Love you!! Smooches back!!" Along with a photo of one of her two new kittens and the caption "Simon says hi."

What Britt didn't know was that, after sending that initial text and movie trailer, I could not sleep. So I followed up minutes after her text message with the following:

Britt - I was looking at flights to Buenos Aires last night to go see Tay Tay in November…does the thought of picking a random country to go see her jam out excite you or make you feel anxious? Cuz I'd fly us somewhere to see her if you were down

I anticipated a "no, too anxious…" response, but I had to ask! (*the next 4 are Britt, back-to-back, while I'm showering for work…*)

Am I a boring old frump if I say anxious? Long flights are so hard on my bad knees (grandma emoji) But that sounds amazing!!!…

But the Europe leg id be more open too cuz I think that's only like a 5 hour flight-ish vs Buenos Aires is probably more like 10 hours

Omg you & me as international Swifties does sound amazing tho!!!!! (plane & heart emoji)

But that is expensive. I would love love to come to Raleigh & see the Tay Swift movie together in theaters tho! We could get dressed up and be crazy in the theater!! Lol

I wrote back at 8:51 AM,

I would fucking lovvveee that!!!!!

And from there, Britt's text messages were all about what outfit she was going to wear, the beaded bracelets we needed to make to hand out at the theater, and about booking the tickets to fly to see me…and Taylor…in Raleigh! It's funny. She sent another text message later that day that read…(*her husband's name is Forrest…):

"I was just texting Forrest about it before but he finally got out of his meeting so he called me and literally said "You and Bruce need this. Taylor Swift is your religion" hahaha so he's very supportive…"

And from there, the flight was booked, movie tickets were purchased, and I ordered A LOT of lettered beads off Amazon.

3 days later, Jon and I spent just enough time together for me to get energized and motivated to write 2 books. It was an intense meeting.

It's amazing when something creative is born from something terrible…

CHAPTER 30

......•.•.•.......

You're A Bad Idea

So I walk outta here tonight
Try to go on with my life
And you can say, "We're still friends"   **(I don't wanna**
pretend)
So if I see you again....
Don't you
Don't you smile at me and ask me how I've been...
                    -**Don't you**, Taylor Swift

This most recent visit to see Blackie and Brownie, Jon and Guy, was over Labor Day weekend, on Sunday, September 3rd, 2023. I attended a Sunday afternoon cookout with my kickball team in Raleigh, and as we were headed to the team captain's community pool, I got a text from Jon. I told him I would come to town for what was left of the long weekend, so his text was simply inquiring about my ETA. I told my team goodbye, jumped in the car, and started off on the hour-forty-five minute trek.

Coming into town on the Sunday of a long weekend, I knew it would just be an overnight stay since I'd have to be back home for work Tuesday morning. I left my dogs back in Raleigh since Pebbles and Layla tend to be a bit too energetic for Blackie and Brownie (, plus they pee on anything they mistake for a pee pad – which includes all of Jon's white bathroom mats as well as the carpet in his closet, apparently).

I arrived at Jon's late afternoon, grabbed my bag from the trunk, and headed back to the pool house.

CLOSURE

When Jon first came out to the pool house, we started chit-chatting about life and the dogs. He asked me about work, and I told him I was still seeing a lot of clients, as mental health help is still in high demand. He started talking about nearly firing the nightclub manager the previous night for coming to work drunk.

Then he started laying in on Kris and his boyfriend. They've been tasked with cleaning the club between nights it's open and have been doing so for years. And doing so poorly, always, according to Jon's assessment. This was not news – it is something Jon speaks about frequently to anyone in earshot. I don't know how often he tells them directly that they need to do a better job, but anyone close to Jon has heard about the flaws in their performance. This is not unique to Kris or his partner. This is Jon, with every employee. If you're doing a good job, he just never mentions you.

As Jon was speaking about the underperformance of Kris & Co., I made a joke that, *of course,* they were disappointing him. After all, if he hired someone who did a great job, then what would he have to talk about? (He seemed to accept that as a fair point.) I went on to say that because they were living in such close proximity to *him,* they were doomed to fail. Jon, being the quizmaster he is, wanted to know what I meant by that. I relayed to him that, essentially, he is an iceberg, sinking the ships of his closest friends and boyfriends - generally, anyone who gets too close to him. I let him know that I was once one of those sinking ships, so I knew what I was talking about. But having moved away, I'd been able to get my boat patched up and was back to smooth sailing. (I was impressed with myself as I put together that metaphor right there on the spot!) I then started backtracking, explaining that I was just kidding and that I really wasn't trying to get into anything 'heavy.' I quickly apologized for even mentioning it and tried to play it off like I didn't mean it and was just kidding.

As I mentioned in the prequel to this book, I don't like saying anything behind someone's back if I haven't said it directly to their face. And since breaking up with Jon, I have shared with him many times that I wished he'd pay more attention to his influence on impressionable young men around him (…and notice that he's a negative/bad influence. And then do better.) Because everything I knew and liked about myself warped into something ugly during my years with Jon. And it wasn't until I got away from him that I started to like myself again. If I had listened to people, it could've all been avoided.

I could've left sooner.

CHAPTER 31

•••••••••••••••••

Tolerate It

When I was with Jon, he would talk about his exes. From time to time, he'd spell out that they'd each become increasingly less productive, less cheerful, more dependent on alcohol and drugs, and more paranoid and distrustful. The idea of there being a common denominator never really hit me. But I know *why* it never hit me: because the way Jon would tell it, each of his former boyfriends became his burden to bear – after all, he was the one having to deal with the messes they'd turned into during the time they dated. The person, who he'd initially thought was worthy of moving onto his property, had, by Jon's account, *proven* to be problematic…Not at first, mind you…but every one of them (us!) turned toxic, and Jon – the innocent bystander – had suffered through the fallout. *This is the overarching story of all of his romantic relationships. To be clear, no one is their best self when they date Jon. You may be your best self going into the relationship, but by the time it's coming to an end, you're smoking crack and pounding on his door, or you're an alcoholic who catches him cheating, or you're headbutting glass doors while he's fucking your best friend, or you're a multi-year meth user punching him in the shoulder while he's driving…It is impossible to flourish in the environment he creates for a lot of reasons. But then, when the dude's spirit is dead and/or he's 'aged out,' Jon usually does something to cause the relationship to implode. It's been a pattern with Jon for as long as I've known him, and he and I met in 2007. He either does not learn from his mistakes, or it is no mistake at all (…**mastermind**…?) – but more of an intentional plan that he has perfected and that gets him what he wants every time…

When you get away from the iceberg and patch your boat, you give yourself a fighting chance at doing great things, reclaiming your self-confidence, and recognizing that whatever dependence you believed you had on this person was the problem and not the solution.

But back to my recent visit to see Jon and us standing out back in his pool house. Jon and I continued chatting, and as I was wrapping up my 'harder truth' Iceberg theory about Jon dragging down the people who are closest to him, his boyfriend came out of the house and started walking towards the pool house. "Oh look, here comes one of the 'winners' now…" Jon commented.

CHAPTER 32

••••••••• ● ••••••••

Can We Have...Nice Things?

Guy made it back to the pool house. Jon's boyfriend is someone I like as a person. Which kind of sucks because I initially thought that if I either didn't like him OR simply avoided getting to know him at all, I'd feel less inclined to provide him any insight into who he was dating and just let him figure it out for himself.

Seated inside the pool house, Jon led the conversation with his quizmaster-style questions. I was in the hot seat on one side of a couch with Guy sitting on the other and Jon in a nearby chair. It was the three of us sitting around the pool house. Moods were good. The dogs were there too, so that made me happy.

Jon began making inquiries about my experience from day-to-day as a therapist. In typical Jon fashion, these were not open-ended questions and did not come across as being born from genuine curiosity. I told him I'd reduced my hours intentionally because, for a while there, I'd been seeing eleven clients a day, and that was just too much to be sustainable.

He asked if I got sick of listening to people's problems all day long...if I ever just wanted to tell them to shut the fuck up, quit their bitching and just get over it. Now, as an ethically practicing therapist, "no" was my response, explaining that I still genuinely like helping people and that even with the most difficult clients, when I get to know their story better and why they are the way they are, feeling empathy for what they're dealing with develops, naturally. Jon pressed the issue, asking if I didn't get tired of people coming in with the same sob stories week after week. I told him that, actually, one of my favorite parts of the job was seeing my clients genuinely get better – meeting their goals – and feeling better about themselves and their situations. (It was around this time that I sensed Jon was not getting what he was looking for from my responses.) He shifted gears.

Jon wanted to know how long I worked with clients, generally...weeks? Months? Number of sessions? That kind of thing. I let him know that it varied, with some people meeting their initial goals quickly and others taking more time.

I used the example of people who come in for ADHD coaching versus therapy, noting that the coaching work I do with these clients is more often time-limited, given that we get through the various parts of the slide show I'd created over some number of sessions. When the client demonstrates that they've absorbed the information and are practicing some of the strategies in their day-to-day life and finding things are generally better, we wrap up. Sometimes, there will be a check-in or two just to ensure they're continuing to practice what they've learned, but ADHD coaching is typically more time-limited from the onset.

Jon responded by asking if I thought he had ADHD, to which I responded that yes, he absolutely has ADHD. I went on to explain why having ADHD is not necessarily a bad thing – in fact, in certain careers, it's advantageous. I let him know that people with ADHD are highly intelligent and typically more creative than neurotypical people. It doesn't make sense to me that there are so many other diagnoses in the DSM-5, and yet ADHD is the only one that includes such stigmatizing language – using both "deficit" and "disorder" as part of the label. I continued on with my speech about why ADHD is not actually the problem – it's really the American school system that is the problem, expecting people with ADHD to conform to the style of learning rather than supporting a student's unique learning style with more hands-on teaching that isn't so easy to become distracted from.

Jon wanted to know more about how I'd reached my conclusion for him, specifically, to which I reminded him that I had seen his report card from school, which included an array of letter grades that fall within the alphabet's first six, minus any "A's" (or "E's"). More specifically, there was a note from the teacher explaining that Jon was thriving socially but couldn't be made to focus on anything he didn't want to focus on and noting that he was disruptive. I then ran through some ADHD symptoms off the top of my head, posing them as questions with two choices, and let Jon pick his answer. Basic things, like if he preferred reading from textbooks or experiential learning, if he preferred to sit still or be actively moving as a kid and present-day, etc.

I didn't mention this in the moment, but it did flash through my mind: One time, Jon's best friend Jean started fussing at him in the kitchen because as the two were standing up and Jean was telling a story, Jon was rocking back and forth, unconsciously. Staying still is not something Jon does, except for when he is hyperfocused on something he's interested in. Which is what his next question was about – if he had ADHD, how come he could focus for hours on certain things? I let him know that hyperfocus is also an ADHD symptom. And the fact that he's late to most things is also symptomatic. Jon concluded by stating that he wasn't sure if he had "AHD" or not, " but appreciated the information. I concluded by letting Jon know that his meth use actually made a lot of sense in that people with ADHD often function better on stimulant medication, and since meth is in the same category as meds prescribed for ADHD, his preference for and use of uppers over downers may even be symptomatic of untreated ADHD.

We reverted back to the trajectory of therapy clients coming in seeking services. I let Jon know that, again, everyone's needs are different, so there's no exact way of knowing how many sessions someone may need when they begin therapy. Some people drop out of therapy, and you never really know why. As long as there was not a safety concern, I just had to hope they were out there, living their best lives. And if they ever came back in for therapy, I'd be happy to see them. I went on to say that it had dawned on me that many of the clients I see had accomplished their initial goals for therapy, but for whatever reason, they chose to continue meeting with me, often regularly, but sometimes with more time in-between sessions.

Jon jumped on this, questioning if I ever tried to convince clients they needed to keep coming to therapy because I wanted their money, even though I knew they didn't need therapy anymore. I let him know that, no, that wasn't a thing – there is enough demand for mental health help that if I terminate with a client, the spot will get filled, one way or another. *If I thought Jon cared to hear it, I would have explained why it would be completely unethical to practice the way that he was suggesting, but that would have been a mood killer, and Jon would have undoubtedly lost interest quickly and cut me off with a new, more interesting question. He was asking these questions with a big smile. I don't think he was trying to piss me off. He was just being himself. I don't think he knows just how much our differing values ever really got to me when we dated. I gave up on trying to get him to understand all of that long before we broke up.

He went on to ask questions about how I navigate therapy sessions and if I am frequently pretending to listen to clients while watching porn or online shopping (no...). How about simultaneously seeing two clients on Zoom at once to make more money while not letting either of them know that's what I was doing?? (No...but I at least got a laugh at this suggestion because the idea of doing it was at least funny to imagine...). He posed other questions, suggesting ideas for practicing more lucratively and with less concern for client welfare.

CLOSURE

I know this was just Jon joking around lightheartedly, but because of our history, I get triggered. Not yet, though...I was smiling along with his ridiculous questions, explaining why some were impossible, others were unethical, and others I'd have to think about further...jokingly. But even though part of my brain knew he was kidding, the other half was becoming irritated...and *that* part of my brain said...

What does Jon get out of trying to catch me in some ethical jam-up? Or is he just trying to give me ideas for being more like him? If I look at Jon through the *worst* possible lens, I see the encounter like this: I've made the mistake of telling Jon I'm an especially good therapist, and he's trying to shit on it. This is a small example in the grand scheme of things, but it's things *like this* that show me 1) he doesn't *actually* know me at all and 2) it's partially *my fault* he doesn't know me, given that I would just overlook so much when we dated, and avoid him rather than have a talk about his 'moral bankruptcy issue.' But fortunately, I have both my logical/rational mind and my emotional mind to draw from...

I guess for the sake of keeping things fair and balanced, if I look at Jon in this conversation through the *best* possible lens, he is just having a lighthearted conversation and is not thinking about the way that his questions are landing when he asks them. Perhaps the idea of a therapist without morals is funny to him, and while he doesn't actually mean for me to be offended, he just finds it humorous to think of all the ways that a therapist could potentially be corrupt (?). And through that lens, I'm left with a slightly different conclusion: 1) no wonder I had to be high all the time to date this guy.

I mostly stay away from Jon because it's hard to be around him for long without me going back into overthinking mode and **looking back in regret,** over the fact that **I ignored when they said run as fast as you can.** We never would have been a good match - our morals and values were always misaligned. But I think at 23 I believed I could shift

89

Jon into a place of at least understanding my values even if not adhering to them. But we never got there. And now, I realize that values aren't something you can compromise when assessing someone's potential to be a long-term partner. Because if overlook this type of inherent difference between yourself and your partner, it's inevitably going to blow up one day…or your own values will have to shift. And that also feels terrible. Recognizing that I was ultimately changing into someone I didn't recognize, someone I didn't like, all just to be with Jon? – that just made me more resentful of him when we were together, as it was happening. And resentment in a relationship is just added toxicity.

CHAPTER 33

······•·•·•·••·•·•·•·•···

Thanks Taylor!

One of the rabbit holes Jon started trying to lead me down during our pool house conversation was suggesting I should be bitter at Taylor Swift for making money off her fans in the US while touring overseas by making a movie of the **Eras Tour** to be released in theaters. I let him know that just a week earlier, I had been looking at plane tickets and concert tickets everywhere she was scheduled on her tour - from Brazil to Australia to Japan — because I wanted to see her live, *somewhere!* I went on to explain that the way I saw it, by making the movie, Taylor was allowing me and all her other fans to still get to see her on tour without breaking the bank. Any true Taylor fan knew that was her goal. Jon's point was more that she was making even more money off of her fans than an artist who was simply touring without a movie. This was when I mentioned to him that she had given $100k to each of the drivers on her tour, proving that she's looking out for her people and fans and that she's a brilliant businesswoman. Everyone ends up happy. (But, as we all know, **haters gonna hate hate hate hate hate...**)

Plus, I would now get to see her on the big screen with my best friend, Britt, who was set to fly into town for the movie's opening weekend! Jon knows Britt. It was hard for me to contain my excitement around this development.

I would have thought Jon knew me better than to come for Taylor...but it felt good being able to defend her awesomeness so easily. I did get a bit defensive when Jon said he thought he'd read that the bus drivers were paid $50k, not $100k. (I don't know why he'd challenge me on something Taylor related…?) As if JC's knowledge of TSwizzle was greater than my own (*big eye roll*). This is Jon in a nutshell, as he will bring up some **contrarian shit even on topics like mental health, therapy, and Taylor Swift – 3 things I know A LOT more about than he does, obviously… Looking back on this moment now, I wish that when Jon began scrutinizing my words on this evening in his pool house, my immediate reaction was simply one of silent gratitude. That way, Jon could just be Jon, and I could just be grateful I got away.

I'm sure if I hadn't **tolerated it** for 6+ years in a relationship, Jon wouldn't bother me nearly as much as he does. But he still has a way of making me feel unseen and unheard, just like he did when I was living there with him. But a partner should never make you feel unseen and unheard. Ever. And he did it consistently. I let him do it, by not leaving. So, while I find great relief in the fact that he's not my partner anymore, his present-day behaviors serve as a trigger for a lot of feelings within me that never were resolved.

Again, I could have left much sooner than I did. I should have.

But if I had, what would I be writing about now?

CHAPTER 34

••••••••• ● ••••••••

Quit the Mental Gymnastics
and Mind Fucks

Conversation had gotten a bit more tense at this time, although I don't remember what we were discussing. Jon's partner, Guy, excused himself to go to the bathroom. I reminded Jon that we didn't need to talk about anything that created tension or friction – especially not in front of Guy. (*I realize now that I do too much trying to protect Guy from discomfort. I am constantly putting myself in Guy's shoes and projecting how I would feel in the same circumstance onto him. I found myself thinking, "I wouldn't want to hang with my current boyfriend and his ex, if they're talking about certain topics…" But I am not a mind reader, and I don't need to protect Guy from anything. He's 28 currently and can make his own decisions.

In previous visits, I had seen Jon and Guy get into an argument or two. And this day in the pool house would not be the first time that Guy witnessed tension between Jon and me.

I used to feel like Jon enjoyed conflict. Now, I think he just hates when I set a boundary by suggesting we <u>not</u> discuss something – whatever it may be. Multiple times on this evening, when we were chatting out in the pool house, I suggested things like, "Jon, we don't need to keep talking about *this* (your defects as a boyfriend)…Especially since Guy is going to hear whatever we're discussing when he comes out of the bathroom. He doesn't need to hear *that…*" But in these instances, Jon would insist we keep talking it out…

I was trying to make it clear that my goal had not been to come into town and debate or argue with Jon. I reminded Jon that we could change topics to anything that wouldn't cause friction…anything at all…

Jon insisted it was fine. He noted that this conversation so far had helped him to realize something - that I had the *wrong* impression of him. To have a "wrong" impression of Jon was a joke – it'd be different if I didn't know him well. But I think what Jon ultimately meant by that comment was that I don't have the impression of him he wants me to have. And that, I'm certain, is true.

"Jon, do you realize that in the entire time I have known you, you've _never_ admitted you were wrong? Like….for *anything…*" (Jon was not about to get away with *my impression* being what was the problem, here.)

Jon insists I don't know what I'm talking about – he says he admits to being wrong "all-the-time!" It must have just been my misperception or me misremembering things.

That's when Guy emerges from the bathroom, having no idea what we've been chatting about. Jon looks at Guy and asks, "Babe, I have no problem admitting when I'm wrong…right?" Guy starts in with, "Well, you've never said you were *wrong* since I've met you…I mean, I've definitely not *heard* you say *that* before…but *maybe* before we dated, you were wrong about something…?"

But honestly, baby, who's counting?...Who's counting? 1..2..3. If that's point 1, my next point was scored when I said to Jon the exact same thing, this time about apologies – how he never apologizes for anything he does wrong in a relationship. Same song and dance from Jon – sure I do! I'm pretty sure I apologized for *something* to *someone*. Why, *just last week,* I think it was! Then he asked Guy – who appeared to be totally checked-out of our conversation, "Babe, I apologize to you, right?" Guy responded, "I mean…no…not since we've been dating…ever…" (score: point 2). And just to drive the nail home, I asked Guy, "And, to be clear, he *has* done *things* for

94

which he *should have* apologized since y'all got together...?..."
Guy, "Oh yeah, definitely. He's for sure done things he *should
have* apologized for..." (point 3...**but honestly baby, who's
counting?**).

I realized at this time that I was getting too big for my
britches and that this was only going to keep going downhill.
I said, "let's talk about something else! Anything!..." But no,
Jon wanted to stay the course – while still letting me know
along the way either that I'm wrong or maybe saying, "I'm
sorry you have this false perception of me." I knew I wanted
off this ride...

And while I shouldn't have turned into a show-off, it
felt like too opportune a moment to let slip by...(*since I
don't know anything about the psychology of Jon, it
shouldn't really matter anyway, right?)

Guy was either looking at his phone or flipping
through a magazine when he said, "Hey Jon, look at this!
What do you think about putting LED lights in the pool??"
Guy had unknowingly set me up to teach him something
about Jon that he could use to his advantage one day. Jon
already had a "no" look on his face when I said: "Wait!
Pause the conversation. Let me explain how this is going to
play out...then I'll teach you how to approach this differently
if you actually want to get Jon to do something *like* installing
LED lights in the pool." I got Jon to confirm he was going
to shoot the idea down, and then I proceeded to explain,
"Jon <u>does not</u> like any ideas that are not his own. However,
that doesn't mean you can't get him to make an idea of yours
happen. You just have to approach it differently. If you want
Jon to install LED lights in the pool, you have to start waaay
far away from the idea itself. You'd need to ask Jon, "what's
an LED light?" – even if you already know the answer. Then,
you'd inquire, "Do you think anyone has ever used an LED
light under water?" Then let Jon explain from there...*then*,
the next time you're walking by the pool at night with Jon,
you need to say, "Gee, this pool sure is dark..." I went on to
tell Guy that there's a good chance the pool would be

outfitted with LED lighting overnight – it just has to be Jon's idea (*or he at least needs to *believe* it's his idea).

While having to play games like this can be frustrating in a relationship, once you figure out how to do it, it's not such a pain. But for the time period where you just feel like your ideas are never good enough for Jon, it can feel pretty terrible. And while in most relationships, I would never advise people on how to manipulate their partners, with Jon, it was necessary in order to hold on to my sanity and my self esteem. I knew better than to think that only Jon had worthwhile ideas. I'm not sure if this wasn't *as bad* at the beginning of our relationship or if it had been just as bad, but it didn't irritate me as much in the early days.

Back to the pool house: I knew things were going sideways. I brought hilarious porn with me for Jon and I to laugh about, and the vibe was way far from where it needed to be in order for these videos to be as funny as I thought they were…I became insistent we talk about something other than Jon's quirks. And Jon obliged…

Well, then…start the videos! He insisted… (*I had NOT intended on watching these with Guy present. I mean, I didn't care that he was there. I just figured he wouldn't want to see his current boyfriend having sex with his ex.)

We watched. We laughed. It was embarrassing but funny. Guy tried to leave halfway through, but he only barely made it out the pool house door when Jon insisted he come back in. (Why? I don't know…). The audio was a bit low when truly the whole point was the conversation and not the video…but that was fine (I wasn't going to be like, "Crank the volume!" Because no one needs to hear me shriek).

After the video ended and we were back to chit-chatting, I commented lightheartedly that I respected him for rocking a "rehab t-shirt." His bright neon blue t-shirt said "Canyon Ranch" on the front. *My only context for Canyon Ranch is that it is a place where therapists send people with money to go sober up discretely. And where rich alcoholics from Atlanta tell their friends they're going for 'spa treatments'…* Jon insisted he didn't go there for rehab. I tried to explain that *some* people go there for that reason and that I hadn't meant any offense. But Jon pushed the issue, insisting respectable people – like his eldest sister (who is a judge, so when Jon dropped her name, of course I knew that yes, she *is* a respectable person...) and her husband had been there! There was no point in arguing this further, so I just apologized for calling it a rehab shirt. (I knew he'd been to rehab *somewhere at some point.* He could have just as easily said *where* he went to rehab to clear up the confusion. But instead...) I, essentially, was wrong. (*This all too familiar feeling was back, even though I'd moved two hours away to outrun it.*) It wasn't an argument worth pursuing. **Both of these things can be true** – Jon may have gone there for the spa experience, and other people have gone there to dry out. I can know, internally, that both perspectives and experiences are valid today. I no longer need Jon to validate what I know to be true. In keeping my side of the street clean, it was still a poor choice of words. I really wasn't trying to offend him. But it certainly didn't help the tension in the room.

*In hindsight, the rehab Jon went to had deep sea fishing as an activity, and Canyon Ranch is all about peace and tranquility. It *should have* registered with me that this *was not* Jon's rehab...stupid, stupid, stupid **ME!** It was stupid - I had learned long ago that the less I said to Jon, the less conflict there was. **I shoulda known**... I was operating like I could talk freely...but I needed to remember, ...not without consequences... (Stupid.)

"Cool shirt" would have been a better comment to make.

Since moving away, I found my voice. And I'm allowed to have opinions again! Opinions that don't come with a penalty or backlash. And my thoughts and opinions are respected...even appreciated! It's embarrassing to admit, but the first time my current boss told me, "Bruce, I really appreciate you. I am lucky that we found each other," I started crying. I am so glad this came through in a text message because, at the time, I could not have told you why the tears came up.

But that's eroded self-esteem, baby. Eroded self-esteem...

I forget about you long enough to forget why I needed to...

Luxuryrehabs.com features Canyon Ranch as one of the best...again, I'm not saying that's *why* Jon went there, just that *some* people do go to kick a habit. And when it feels like your ex-partner's goal is to make you feel wrong...even all these years after **we were dead and gone and buried**...sometimes something as dumb as a disagreement over a t-shirt can be an unexpected trigger.

Around this time, Jon announced he was going to walk the dogs. He usually tries to get someone to come with him - and *maybe* he asked - but I don't think he did. I remember him hopping up and just saying, "I'm gonna go walk the dogs," and then going. (I could speculate as to why he didn't extend an invitation, but I won't. I'll just say this is not his typical way of behaving, so interpret from that what you will.)

Guy and I hung back and chatted. Guy started talking about his trip with Jon to Jon's recently acquired property in Mexico. Guy had mentioned last time he came to visit Raleigh that this trip was happening, but at the time, he didn't know Jon had invited his (Guy's) parents as well. Guy said he learned they were coming "the day before" they left. Guy explained that he loves his parents but he wished Jon had been more upfront with the invitation he had extended, as this called for a very different packing list.

Guy went on to say that his parents and others had expressed a range of feelings, from annoyance to concern, over how out-of-touch he had been. I just smiled and nodded while Guy relayed this information. (In these moments I want to say so much, but I really try and practice what I preach. If I told Guy all of the ways I could relate or even said, "Yeah, Jon really sucks sometimes – he's a terrible communicator," THAT would be talking behind Jon's back. So I bite my tongue – and if I'm going to say it, for better or worse, it's going to be with Jon present.)

In my own limited phone communication with Guy, I will say he has some confusing tendencies in regards to disappearing…Like, he texted me, "Hey Bruce, how's your week been?" at 7:15 pm one time, and I responded at 7:15 pm, answering his question and asking how *his* week had been. He didn't get back to me for almost 24 hours. Which was fine. But he and I don't have the type of relationship where we just chit-chat about our weeks, so it was strange. (Why ask if you aren't going to look at your phone or reply, even if I responded that quickly?) I'm just throwing that out there because he does have abnormal texting patterns. (*The example above is just one of many.) He apologizes for being "bad at communicating" in a few of his texts to me, and, as I mentioned, we don't text very much.

I watched Rob distance himself from people when he was with Jon. I know I definitely did that. And now Guy is telling me people are getting on him about doing it…Don't get it twisted: Jon NEVER told me to distance myself from friends and family. It's weird, though - it happens. And to be clear, none of my friends or family were ever like, "Don't be with Jon!" so it's not like *that* was why I did it.

Guy explained that he was appreciative of Jon's being thoughtful by inviting his parents, although he didn't understand why he didn't tell him about it. "But, y'all had fun?" was my only response. I was mentally drawing parallels to my own experience but didn't want to get caught up in more uncomfortable conversations. "Yeah, we had fun."

Jon didn't communicate this to Guy for one reason or another. Maybe it just slipped his mind. Maybe there was some other reason and Jon *was* intentionally being deceptive. Either was possible. But since I was trying to maintain the peace, I figured exploring this further with Guy would be a poor choice on my part. (So I resisted my natural tendency to go into therapist mode).

There's a world in which Guy's parents and Jon were in touch enough for Jon to know that they didn't like that their son was MIA, and so Jon invited them without letting Guy know that was the plan. For that reason. But it's also entirely possible that it slipped Jon's mind that he had invited them. Or that he thought he had told Guy sooner and hadn't realized he'd failed to mention it. Or that he'd impulsively invited them at the last minute, and that's why Guy was also learning they were coming at the last minute. When Guy found out they were coming, he learned it from his parents. Maybe Jon meant it to be a surprise for Guy? Oddly as that would be, since Jon himself hates surprises (although he will not admit it. But he does…). *There are probably other possible reasons why it played out the way that it did. These are just the possibilities that come to my mind most immediately.

(I know which of those *I* believe is true…and I know which of those I think Jon would tell Guy was true…but since I am trying to stick to what *actually* happened and not get too lost in speculation, I'm going to keep that to myself.)

While Jon was out on his walk, Guy also brought up his face splinters. These splinters came from being hit with a palm branch while working with Jon some number of years ago. Guy believes splinters from this event have been slowly pushing themselves out of his skin since it happened, and while Jon initially thought that *maybe* some splinters may have entered Guy's skin, over time, Jon has decided that if there ever were splinters, they certainly aren't lodged in his skin anymore and that Guy is delusional. Jon has encouraged others (me) not to engage in speaking about this topic with Guy, and Jon and Guy do not speak about it anymore as it has caused a lot of discord in their relationship. And while I would love to never speak about it again, Guy brings it up *almost* every time I see him…(and literally every time I'm around him for over an hour). Guy shared his perspective with me, feeling hurt when Jon refused to help Guy remove the splinters anymore and even more so when Jon declared that there were no splinters, period. Jon flipped the script and made it clear to Guy that he didn't believe what he was saying was based on reality. Guy had done research and printed out articles that showed that palm splinters can get stuck in human skin in a way that is much different from typical wood splinters. (He had shown me these articles during a previous visit.) So Guy had been hurt by Jon withdrawing his support around this topic, especially because up until that point, he'd felt he and Jon were on the same page about most things.

While I recognize that Guy's circumstances are completely different than anything I ever went through with Jon, the *feeling* you get when you lose Jon's support and things flip in an instant —now that I could relate to. I felt that feeling over the police brutality incident and the Officer Dudley issues that came up in my relationship with Jon. And maybe it's a stretch, but Guy described his experience of Jon changing his tune, and for me, it resonated. While I also kept these thoughts to myself in this moment, hearing that Guy's emotional experience with Jon left him feeling disconnected from Jon in a similar way as how I had felt years prior was disappointing – I knew that feeling **all too well,** and I hated that feeling – for me and for Guy.

I used to know my place was a spot next to you, now I'm searching the room for an empty seat, cuz lately I don't even know what page you're on...

Jon returned from his walk with the dogs. From there, I couldn't tell you what kicked off the unpacking, but Jon and I had what I later described as our **All Too Well** moment – where we unpacked almost every major event in our relationship, sharing our perspectives on what happened and what went wrong, why we didn't feel understood at the time, and even the details of the events – as we remembered them – all these years later. **Maybe we got lost in translation, maybe I asked for too much, but maybe this thing was a masterpiece, 'til you tore it all up. -All Too Well**, Taylor Swift.

I pulled Guy into it when Jon and I were talking about my arrest and the police's use of excessive force. I reminded Jon of when I felt he turned on me (the first time) and compared it to Guy's splinter situation. [The next day, Jon sent me a text message that included, "I thought it was genius comparing the splinters to the St. Patrick's Day incident to foster some support. I'm sure opening that wound by inferring your support that he was wronged put a little air back in that unfortunate problem," – to which I informed Jon that Guy had been talking about the splinters right before he returned from the dog walk. Because I didn't bring that up out of nowhere, but Jon assumed I had. I tried to help Jon understand that it was the same <u>feeling</u>, but I think Jon was still processing the fact that Guy brought up the splinters in the first place. *I am uncertain if the idea of Guy and I having a similar 'feeling' despite it being in response to different events made sense to Jon. Jon's irritation around the conversation remained, although he sounded like he was lightening up a little bit as we were speaking on the phone.

That part about the police and splinters came toward the end of our unpacking that night in the pool house. It was a heated conversation, with Jon talking about things he wasn't physically present to have witnessed as if they were facts. And me, misremembering where I'd been flying off to and for what, as we picked apart an incident from early in our relationship – but Jon remembered where I'd been heading and why. We combed through plenty of the major events we'd gone through together. (And anything we left out I've done my best to include in the two books I've written since that night in the pool house, which was just shy of 2 months ago.)

It was not fun.

And you know, in your soul, when it's time to go...

CHAPTER 35

·······•·•·•·········

Compare and Contrast

Here's what I know: I know how I changed internally while in a relationship with Jon. And I have email records where Jon noted I had changed during that time. I also have memories of the ways that Rob changed when he was with Jon – although admittedly, I didn't attribute the changes I saw in Rob to being something Jon caused at that time. I have my own observations of Jon's current boyfriend – Guy – as well as the things Guy has said to me directly. This chapter will include my own experience, along with my direct observations of the other two and things they have told me directly.

When Rob and Jon were dating, and Rob lived with Jon, he was more reclusive, and his general demeanor shifted. He was less eager to go out and spend time with friends and less jovial. Hell, Jon had to give him meth along with the instruction to go spend time with a friend, and then he'd have me call Rob 'coincidentally.' From my outside perspective, I figured the shift in Rob was more of a 'Rob thing' than a Jon thing and that either not dealing meth anymore made him less social or that something with his mental health had shifted (like, he was off his meds? Maybe?...). Jon used to tell me Rob's mental health was unstable, just like he used to tell Kris and Keeley – like we were all Rob's guardians. And this was long before Jon and I got together that he used to express these concerns...It all came to add up when Rob headbutted the pool house's glass door, and Jon's assertion proved accurate: Rob was mentally unstable. He'd been more withdrawn ever since he'd moved into Jon's place. I didn't get the sense that Rob liked me any less, but there was a noticeable change in how he interacted with people in general. He laughed a lot less. His mood was heavier. And, oh yeah, his headbutting incident happened so that Jon could see how much pain he was in…

As for me, I think how I was during the years I lived at Jon's house may be much better documented in the emails from the last book, as there is a lot of this time period that I just do not accurately remember. Jon's perspective on how I changed may be a better representation, given that I can only speak to how I felt internally and not so much how others perceived me… I'm certain things about me from back then were different. I would still go out to the club with Jon and generally be myself as people knew me, but I became less and less likely to engage with friends that I had made before dating Jon. I didn't have people over (as it had created more issues than it was worth…) or call people on the phone to check in. I became more caught up in hobbies that kept me from being my typical, extroverted self. Nothing was any different for me when I was at work, as I was a hotel front desk person who took pride in his reputation, so I would go into work mode. But at home, I didn't feel particularly happy, and so extra interaction with others was more taxing. (PS- *This is not like me.) And it wasn't just friends. I wasn't in touch with family much either. I'd pick up their calls, but it was during this time period when I stopped making the initial effort myself.

I can't say I've met any of Guy's friends. Assuming they exist, I'd only be speculating as to why he hasn't had them over, but in the times I've visited when Jon was out of town and in the times Jon has been in town, Guy doesn't seem to be spending any more time with people than I used to back then…But it's entirely possible that the reasons why I was 'that way' aren't the same as Guy's reasons…or Rob's reasons…but the behavior *looks* similar. (Come to think of it, if you read **Better Man**, you may recall that I mentioned meeting Jon a few times early in the book and that I'd heard he had a live-in boyfriend named Mark, *but I hadn't ever met him*...I have no clue if that was Mark being reclusive / less social like the rest of us or if we never crossed paths for some other reason. He was not with Jon out at the bar, but again, to lump him in with the rest of us because he wasn't around a few times would be premature and purely speculative.)

When I scroll far enough back through Facebook, I have wall posts and messages from people who are asking, "Why can't I get in touch with you?" and saying, "I miss you...call me!..." etc. It seemed I was missing in action from a lot of my friendships between when I began living with Jon and when I moved out to start my internship in 2013. This is not Jon's *fault*, but more just a pattern I see in myself and in other people Jon dates.

Jon will say his boyfriends become less social because of meth. He said it to me, about me, as he kept giving me more meth. It's worth noting that Rob was on meth when he moved in with Jon, so his shift in mood can't be so easily blamed on drugs. Let's be honest and put it all on the table: when I was with Jon, I was addicted to meth, Percocet, and gambling/online poker...All of which were only accessible in my life because of Jon. I'd never been in a situation before where I had unlimited access to meth until I was with Jon. No one gave me Percocet daily in my life before Jon (nor has anyone since). And I didn't know anything about gambling or that online gambling was a real thing that people did until I was dating someone who did it every day.

A clueless person may get the impression that you-win-some-you-lose-some and that gambling kind of just balances itself out, over time. I was that clueless person. And to hear Jon talk about trips to Vegas and Atlantic City, you would think that the wins and the losses from his trips did balance out. For most people, this is not the case. The idea that people come out 'about even' is false. If that were the case, places like Vegas would not exist. But I guess if **you play stupid games, you win stupid prizes.**

I do not have any idea how much Jon gambles these days. But at the beginning of our relationship, it was an all-day-every-day ordeal for him, waiting for the next tournament to start and going on the roller-coaster of being 'up' in the tournament standings only to eventually 'bust out.' I didn't know any poker terms going into this relationship – the turn, the river, pocket aces...that the worst hand in Texas Hold 'Em to start with is a 2-7 off-suit...None of this registered when I met Jon. And it's all useless knowledge in my head now since I no longer play in person or online. And thank god for that – I threw away so much time and money on this 'activity'. It is beyond embarrassing. If I knew nothing about poker at all, present day, my life would be completely unaffected. I would just have a much bigger bank account and much less regret over falling into such a useless hobby. Gambling exists solely to take advantage of people and the dopamine rush that comes along with the highs and the desperate feelings associated with the lows. Gambling does not exist for people to make it lucrative – it's a losing battle. And when your boyfriend does it all the time, and he's successful (*in life, not necessarily at gambling), it's easy to get the false impression that gambling and being financially successful are not mutually exclusive. For me – these two things are 100% mutually exclusive. **...wish you could go back, and tell yourself what you know now...**

Jon blamed other past boyfriends and their 'shifts in temperament' on different substances prior to meth solidifying its spot as Jon's drug of choice. With Mark, it had been alcohol and cocaine for A.J. I have never heard Jon acknowledge the role he played in making any of these substances available to his exes, just that Mark became a paranoid and suspicious drunk, and A.J. a fiend for crack. And yes, I know people in their 20's *can* make *their own* adult decisions. It's not all Jon's fault. But so much stuff is normalized under Jon's roof that is not normal in other healthy relationships.

CLOSURE

I would argue that if you're 10...20...30...40 years older than your boyfriend, and your boyfriends tend to leave cheated, addicted, and feeling like idiots – each and every time – you are probably a toxic person to date.

Guys wouldn't have the means or the access to a consistent drug supply without Jon...

It's been decades of him practicing this same pattern in relationships...

At what point does Jon become the **anti-hero**, singing, **it's me, Hi!, I'm the problem, it's me.** He is the common denominator in the addictions, past and present, of several people I know. People I know and care about that never dated him – because he doesn't just get people he's dating into drugs. He does it to poker buddies and certain other 'close' friends as well. Some of these people have moved on from him and his town. Others still live on his property...But if, by Jon's own account, every guy he dates loses his luster at some point (be that his self-esteem or that zest for life he once had), and then Jon loses interest...is that okay? Is it okay for a wealthy man who is now in his 60s to have a strung-out-20-something-year-old-boyfriend by his side for decades, with the only thing that changes is who that boyfriend is and sometimes which drug the dude is strung out on?

CHAPTER 36

•••••••• • •••••••

Bad Influence

I have tried to talk to Jon about the influence he has on other people, especially since breaking up, in calm and peaceful exchanges. He responded one time with, "I am not oblivious to the influence I have on people and do have regrets. I have tried to make sure that the guys I've been involved with were here for the right reasons and made sure they would have a no-fault off ramp that would allow them to depart without fear of being able to move forward comfortably and not feel trapped by financial or other potential manipulations. Relationships are by their very nature a give and take, and achieving balance is not always achievable. I am aware that in most of my relationships, I have had the upper hand on influence, and I do try not to take advantage of that."

But if you say that, and yet you still drag people down, what good is it doing, 'not being oblivious?' Some people may surmise that - in the words of Eminem - you "just don't give a fuck…" I think what Jon also fails to recognize is that once someone is hooked on drugs supplied by their wealthy boyfriend, the idea that they are going to "comfortably move forward and not feel trapped by financial or other potential manipulations" has already gone out the window. Especially if they've become isolated from the support network they had before getting together with Jon. And if they gave up their housing to move in – there's another complicating factor. Not to mention, I know from firsthand experience there is a tremendous difference between breaking up with Jon *before* he's ready for it to be over (correction: *trying* to break up with Jon before he's ready for it to be over...) versus after he's ready for it to be over. He doesn't build the convenient off-ramp until *he's* ready – it's not how it sounds in how he wrote it.

Any time I have called Jon out directly, especially now that I'm not his partner, it ends in me feeling frustrated. Over text, it's better because I don't see him immediately dismiss what I'm saying. Face-to-face is when it gets bad. He'll disagree with my words, challenge them, play devil's advocate, whatever... But since he's still a quizmaster to his core, he doesn't want to change the topic of conversation. He doesn't give any indication he thinks I have any valid points (*at least not in the moment*), challenging them and shooting them down. And this is incredibly frustrating. Less so now, because I don't need Jon to agree with me on any of the points I'm making – to me, they're facts. There's no world in which he could argue that he makes a positive impact on people without me laughing hysterically. But I don't think he'd try. There was a time when it mattered to me if Jon saw where I was coming from. Now it's unimportant – we aren't together, and he can think **I'm obsessive and crazy, that's fine, you won't mind if I say...by the way...** (While I'm not going to burn all of his pictures,) Now, I'm just interested in healing from him completely. And that's what this has been about – a journey to share my truth and to heal.

I know I cannot change anyone's behavior other than my own. But I also know that Jon has a lot of influence over people that I care about. Which is why, generally, I know I need to stay away from him – because if the whole 'situation' is out of sight, it's easier to keep it out of mind. Spending any more of my time trying to change a distant ex-boyfriend - when I couldn't get him to change when we were together – would just be silly.

But when you finally accept that you can't change the beast, perhaps your best bet is to warn the townspeople instead...

BRUCE LANGDON

CHAPTER 37

•••••••• • •••••••

I didn't have it in myself to go with grace...

I only ended up staying on Jon's property that day for a total of about four hours. Jon sent me an email titled, "Fuck W--------- and the x boyfriends that live there..."

Here's what the email from Jon said:

Sept 4th, 2023 @ 11:59 am:

I'm glad you feel better after a full afternoon and evening of laying out what you believe are some of my many flaws. I think a lot of what you point out and harbor resentment towards me are really just the inability understand each other. for example when i want to engage on a subject and offer a different opinion or maybe ask questions to get better insight, in my mind i'm just engaging in conversation. you may think i am trying to argue with you or somehow am saying im right and you are wrong. talking about **taylors drivers bonuses** you said she gave them 100,000 i said i thought it was 50,000. you are ready to end the convo as if my recollection was an argument. i just wanted to know what the right number was and didnt care who was right .

consequently there were a lot of conversations that were similarly cut short due to differences in how we view a conversation vs an argument.

some of those convos that were cut short may have you believing i was taking a contrary position on subjects we may have been in total agreement.

I don't know how many times tonight you decided to end a conversation that you brought up which did little to resolve the issues.

while i am glad that you feel better having gotten some stuff off your chest there wasn't anything new about your grievances that hasnt already been rehashed more than a few times.

i do want to make a final attempt to at least try to get you to understand my position on the roadblock even if you do not agree or recall it the same way. here it goes.... you got stopped at a roadblock and regardless of what happened between the stop and the 6 cops jumping on your back it could not justify their actions. that was and remains my position and i believe u were justified in pursuing excessive force against the police. the story you told me when i picked up was you were stopped the cop asked for your license which you did not have he ask for your name and addy went to his car returned and said you have about 5 seconds to provide me with ur correct name or you will ill be arrested. u replied you cant just arrest me. at that point he threw your up against side of the car or hood and somehow you ended on the ground with six cops on top of you.

i questioned you about the 5 seconds comment right before the takedown several times because it was an odd thing to say to someone being fully cooperative.

The next day, and invited Dudley over to try to get advice on the matter. When I arrived, you had already been talking to Dudley and I could tell by the tone that he was taking an adversarial position. I launched with both guns blazing and repeating, basically what you had said to me that happened. When I finished, Dudley said something to the effect of, that's not exactly right, talking to you, you were trying to be evasive to avoid having to identify yourself and give me down there without a ticket. To what you responded with a sheepish well yeah, something to that effect. I was a little shocked since I questioned you on that several times trying to make sense out of the five second comment from the police. But it made sense now. it did not change the fact that I was livid and over the unjustified brutality that you suffered, and the fact that dudley was somehow trying to justify it.

fast forward to dinner with Barton Fields. You were retelling the story to him and he you got to the 5 second part of the story i chimed in the fact that you were being a little evasive about identifying yourself, it was meant to be lighthearted, but also helped complete that story so it made sense, and I didn't realize that there was any dispute that that's what put it happen that didn't change my position about the justification for what they did to you. so i was taken back when you denied what was up until then that point an undisputed fact. How that argument in the restaurant was handled by me could have been handled differently but it did not change the fact that what happened to you was wrong. you took it as a betrayal and it was not.

peoples memories can change over time and it seems we recall things differently on the car to the shop incident. i think you were going to California or someplace with your aunt or a family event. you asked if i could drop your car off at the shop so it could be worked on while u were gone. i was happy to follow you to drop it off and pick you up before u left for ur trip. you wanted it done after you left which i thought was absurd since there was no reason you could not be part of the process as your request would require i find a 2nd person to drop off your car. you could not see that as an overreach of a request. the fact that ultimately by your admission last night that i took smithers and george to drop your car off and not smithers and langdon is no different.

i don't harbor any ill will or rehash that stuff. i may not have been the best boyfriend for you but i have good memories of our time together despite it not being a perfect fit. i remain friend and am sorry i have caused you to carry so much resentment towards me for all these years.

your friend til the end,

-JC Buckets

I read this and then called him. It was a pleasant chat. We had our **All Too Well** moment (*he didn't know what that meant, but that was okay.) Rehashing these things *again* would not have been productive. It's all water under the bridge now – the past can't be undone. I just tried to stress that I had not gone there the previous day with any intention of things popping off the way that they had.

I recognize that I am easily triggered by his behavior and how he communicates because it is like it was when we were dating. I have spent plenty of time beating myself up for not getting frustrated and leaving sooner and for sticking it out with Jon for as long as I did. So now, sometimes, when he talks, the way that he approaches topics, I just feel unsettled. Scratch, unsettled, I feel stupid. Why? Because Jon told me a lot of his flaws in the early days of us dating - He said when he's done with a relationship, he stops trying. He also mentioned that he has a history of behaving in a way that is geared toward getting the other person to end the relationship - essentially by being a terrible boyfriend. So, when I comb through my experience, I think, "Well damn Brucey! Jon told you from the start what this would look like…and he did just like he said he would…So, how can you be mad about it?? He literally told you!!" And then I'm back to square one: feeling stupid.

But back to the email…

Most of my reaction to his email was not worth delving into with Jon, as my goal was to maintain the peace. Some prime examples of trigger points came up for me when I read his email. I would probably have read his words much differently if I hadn't dated Jon. I see some gaslighting, minimizing any parts that paint him in a bad light, and re-writing history. There are a couple of places where he just does not understand what happened (parts that he was not there for…) but he has ended up with a false narrative that he's held onto for many years now, even though his 'facts' are wrong. Which is fine – I'm not even concerned about wrong facts, so much as I am *this* type of not admitting when you're wrong...

Where Jon writes, "How that argument in the restaurant was handled by me could have been handled differently..." This type of shit makes me want to launch back into going point by point and explaining why his email is a bunch of crap. And to be honest, I already wrote that out...but I'm pulling it. Because if you read **Better Man,** you already know the level of minimizing Jon's doing by chalking his behavior that night up to the sentence, "How that argument in the restaurant was handled by me could have been handled differently." (*See **Welcome to New York** chapter.) But that's what it looks like when someone rewrites history, downplaying his own bad behavior. It's what it looks like when someone does not apologize. How Jon experiences remorse, *if* he ever feels remorse, is very different than how I experience it.

He never apologized for yelling "liar" in my face, repeatedly, that night in a New York restaurant. But again, he does not apologize. ("I'm sorry you feel that way..." is even a stretch.)

I WAS SOO PISSED.

**That night, I left the restaurant and went and fucked two of my friends who live in NY, as I mentioned in the last book. What I didn't say was that this was the first time I ever physically cheated on Jon. Because if you're going to do it, go big or go home.

**Ya know, there's many different ways that you can kill the one you love,
The slowest way is never loving them enough.**
    High Infidelity, -Taylor Swift

CHAPTER 38

•••••••• • •••••••

Compromised Morals and Values

Cheating on Jon, or on any boyfriend, for that matter - This is what I mean by compromising my own morals. I'd never cheated on a boyfriend before, Jon — I mean, don't get it twisted. If I'm being completely honest, I had done the following, which some people would say counts as cheating: I had exchanged dick pictures with another dude when I was dating Kris. And I had exchanged emails with dudes from Craigslist when I was with Jon *very* early in our relationship — when no one knew we were dating. And I'd briefly broken up with Jon and flirted with a dude I would have liked to sleep with — but it never happened. And I'd had an emotional affair with Kris McRay when I was dating Jon, and Kris was living in our backyard. But I wasn't someone who physically cheated on boyfriends — until I was. I justified it like this: if he gets to hurt me in so many ways and gets to cheat on me in Vegas with multiple dudes and then brag to a friend about it when he gets home, and he gets to decide I'm going to fuck people I don't want to so he can watch, or bring someone home with us from the club — both without talking to me about it first and put me in other non-monogamous situations that I'm uncomfortable with (because of the lack of communication!), then yeah! I'm going to go have the guaranteed best sex of my life. I <u>very clearly</u> should have broken up with Jon <u>forever</u> and *then* gone and slept with my NY friends — and I should have let Jon go on to Madagascar without me and packed up my shit while he

116

was in Africa. But because Jon had booked the flights and we were already in New York, even without the traditional apology that any decent boyfriend would have offered, I went on with him. And we survived Madagascar together.

I've been disconnected from the person I was before Jon. For the record, Jon is the only boyfriend I've ever cheated on. And I'd like to think if I was even in another relationship where that felt like a viable option, I would end the relationship long before it would get to that point. But as for my mentality, unfortunately, I don't know how to become *un*jaded or 're-optimistic'. A lot of what I gave away in that relationship is priceless. By the end of it, I didn't recognize *me* anymore. It's weird to think of myself at that time and compare him to the hopeless romantic I was going into the relationship with Jon. But I try not to think about that because it's a pretty huge bummer.

I spent a lot of time after Jon and I slept together the first time ruminating on the idea that I was a bad person – I had slept with my best friend's boyfriend, and only bad people did that. Right? It didn't matter to me that I would not have done that had drugs not been involved. And it didn't matter that I'd hung out with Jon in his office plenty of times when Rob was at work, and he'd never offered me GHB before that day. It didn't matter that I was emotional the day that it happened, having just had my heart re-broken. And it doesn't matter now that had I known Jon and I would sleep together if I went to his house that day I would not have gone. None of that matters, given that I cannot rewind time.

If I could reclaim **ME!** from before Jon, I'd be in the shoes of someone who would never fuck their friend's boyfriend. Because I never would have done that, minus the GHB, and I've beaten myself up enough over that. Plus, Rob has forgiven me…and I'm sure he had long before I even considered forgiving myself.

But what if the whole incident that sparked this six-year ordeal was in the hands of a **Mastermind** from the very beginning? ...and it hasn't been until I've sat down and thought about all of this and typed it out that it dawned on me: that is a very real possibility.

Lesson learned? Different people strive to be different things. I've always wanted to be a better man, kind of as part of a lifelong quest. He may have masterminded the start of our relationship, or he may have simply thought giving GHB to me when I was sad was a **nice thing to do.** I'm certain that if he were asked, he would say it was the latter. On this one point, I'd like to give him the benefit of the doubt – not for him, but for me. Because if he did mastermind the whole thing, MAN! I would feel even stupider. And I don't have time for that. (So, if anyone's thinking, 'Bruce, that's what happened...', shh! Keep it to yourself. Because no one *really* knows, except for him.)

*Suggested listen: **Mastermind** -Taylor Swift

CHAPTER 39

.... • ....

I see it all now, it was wrong.

When Jon got released from jail in 2017, about a year and a few months after we'd broken up, I was worried about him, so I reached out to check in. I hoped he had all the support he needed during this difficult time.

I did not have the support I needed surrounding my own arrest. Because he left me - alone – both literally (in court) and figuratively – when I needed support the most. My work friends were all super supportive. They expressed concern and wanted to help - they said they'd testify that I go by "Bruce" and didn't even know I had a different first name if it would help. I told them it wouldn't be necessary but I appreciated it. It would have been nice if *someone* had shown up that day so that when the judge cleared the courtroom for me to go on trial, someone else would have been thinking, "This seems odd..." The judge even stopped the proceedings in the middle when a lost civilian entered the courtroom. We resumed after she made the woman leave. I guess in some towns when you're testifying, and your story involves excessive force and police brutality, they don't allow spectators.

But back to the email...Jon says: "When I want to engage on a subject and offer a different opinion or maybe ask questions to get better insight, in my mind, i'm just engaging in conversation. you may think i am trying to argue with you or somehow am saying im right and you are wrong." Jon went on to say, "Some of those convos that were cut short may have you believing i was taking a contrary position on subjects we may have been in total agreement. I don't know how many times tonight you decided to end a conversation that you brought up which did little to resolve the issues." Now, Jon knows how much he likes to play devil's advocate, and he used to own it. And he <u>was</u> taking contrary positions, left and right...I said Taylor Swift gave all her bus drivers 100k, and Jon said, "I thought I read it was 50k." I said, "People go to Canyon Ranch to dry out", and he said, no-they-don't... *I* didn't. (*both can be true!) I said to Jon, "You never admit you're wrong" and "You never apologize", both of which he refuted, but couldn't identify a time he'd been wrong or anyone he'd ever apologized to... (*to be clear, Jon has done the "I'm sorry you feel that way..." lip-service apology, but never the genuinely remorseful kind. It's the most egregious things he ever did in our relationship – the times he hurt me the most – these are the apologies that never came.) And then his boyfriend unknowingly backed my side of the debate, when Jon solicited his opinion because he felt he'd get some support. And when I changed the subject, I just figured Jon would appreciate the fact that now that we're not dating, neither of us has to have those insanely frustrating conversations anymore – we are both free! The conversation topics I tried to end were the ones about Jon's most aggravating behavior patterns. Like, when I told him he's an iceberg that sinks the lives of people that get too close to him – he seemed okay not unpacking that one any further. I told him I shouldn't have brought that up because I really was just trying to have a light-hearted visit. *We ended that discussion topic because Guy was coming out to the pool house. When most of the 'sinkers' have been Jon's boyfriends and closest friends, letting Guy know he has an anchor tied around his ankle didn't feel like a constructive conversation to continue at that time.* I thought I was doing Jon a favor by trying to change topics of conversation at the times that I did.

Through all of the Taylor talk with Jon, I still had a smile on my face (even if he was spinning her negatively). Actually, in the part where he was inquiring about ethics and therapy, I was smiling through that part of the conversation, too. It was his questioning any statement I made about him and insisting I was incorrect that really drove me crazy that night. Because if Jon doesn't see himself as capable of doing wrong, he is LITERALLY never going to change. My fear is that he's going to keep picking a dude in his early 20's (or younger), getting him hooked on drugs, and infiltrating his mind with negativity (I hope I've done a decent job of spelling out exactly what that looks like), isolating him from friends and family, getting him to participate in things he wouldn't choose to if left to his own devices...and then when the spark that initially attracted Jon to the dude has been extinguished, he'll torpedo the relationship one way or another, then it's on to the next. I spent six years with this man, and he is the most frustrating man to argue with...in all the land. I would have *killed* for even the slightest nod that he felt *bad* about *something* he did in our relationship. Hell, if I'd ever heard him express remorse for anything he'd ever done in *any* relationship, that would be a good start...But again, everyone has been his burden to bear, and when he talks about the chaotic ways that relationships ended, he's almost always laughing about the role that he played while calling out the other person's faults.

There are so many ways that the concept of being 'wrong' can be interpreted in a relationship – I stand by the idea that Jon is not susceptible to *any* of them in his own mind. He *never* got any bleach on any clothing in our laundry, he *never* gave me bad advice or encouraged me to trust someone I should not have, he *never* made a mistake (period), he *never* failed to show up for me, and he *never* did anything but support me and support our relationship – in word and in behavior. In *his* mind, *never*. Because all of that would be *wrong*. This is probably why, towards the end of the conversation in the pool house that night, he made the statement that he has almost exclusively fond memories of our time together and was surprised by how much resentment I seem to carry around. (My response to that is: When you literally have no downtime between relationships

121

to pause and reflect on all of your problematic behaviors, maybe that is what you end up with continued bad behavior in your next relationship and nothing but fond memories after some time has passed! It actually makes a lot of sense – Mark and Rob were fresh when he used to tell me how problematic they were. But when he got to A.J., he said only positive things…then A.J. and I met, and A.J. said a lot of negative things…and when I repeated them to Jon, he dug through all of the sunshine and rainbows in his head, and remembered how A.J. had *actually* not just been the loveable "little joey" who loved the weather channel but *actually* a crack head who begged Jon to stay with him when Jon decided he was done. (I have no way of contacting A.J., but I would love to know if he'd ever smoked crack *before* dating Jon. Given how young he was when the relationship started, I'm sure I know the answer. It would just be nice to get confirmation.)

Side Note:
Dear Reader

Dear Reader,

I just want to delete the rest of this email-back-and-forth bullshit and rehashing the past, but for the sake of trying to give a complete and accurate picture of my perspective on the things that he mentions in his email as well as the events that coincide with what Jon said, I will continue. Also included is the passive aggressive (borderline cunty) response I ended this communication chain with. (*For what it's worth, the emails in both books are not edited for content at all – because it wouldn't be fair to shorten them or alter them if I'm trying to give a complete picture..*) It's just a couple more pages of this…

Back, once again, to explaining his email:

As for the car-drop off 'event' mentioned above, parts of his narrative are either confused or incorrect (I may have *miscommunicated*, but I think he just *misinterpreted*..?). Jon stated (about my car request…), "i was happy to follow you to drop it off and pick you up before u left for ur trip. you wanted it done after you left which i thought was absurd since there was no reason you could not be part of the process." I don't know where Jon is coming up with this, given that the whole reason why I needed his help was because I *didn't* have time to be involved in getting my car to the shop because I had to use my car to drive to and from work, and the check-engine light was on. Then I was catching my flight. I'm not sure if Jon felt it was "absurd" of me to not have time to drop the car before my flight, or "absurd" to ask my boyfriend for a favor (?). Or perhaps I am more demanding and entitled than I realize, and it was an "absurd" request? I mean, I would do it for someone…(?) I knew it was a favor I was asking, which afforded Jon every right to say "no", he couldn't do it. So, since he said "no", instead I asked Officer Smithers if he could get it done, and he said "yes." Yay! I found someone (else) to do it. I needed it done. It didn't matter to me *who* did it, and if I had the time, I would have. I suppose I could have waited until I got back from California to go drop it off with Jon to get it fixed (*this was pre-Uber*), but that would have left me without a car for as long as it was being worked on. Since I'd be gone a week, I just really appreciated that it got taken care of while I was away. So, thank you to Officer Smithers! I do not know why this was important to bring up (since in the grand scheme of our relationship, this was just a blip on the radar to me), but that is what happened. I know it wasn't Jon's responsibility to get it done, but I asked him originally because his assistant at the time, a nice guy from Africa (nicknamed George), lived on the property and regularly helped Jon do just about anything. He also drove Jon's truck plenty. To this day, in the same circumstances, I would ask my boyfriend if he could make it happen before I'd ask a friend. And Smithers figured out how to make it happen and got it taken care of.

When Jon says in the email, "the fact that ultimately by your admission last night that i took smithers and george to drop your car off and not smithers and langdon is no different." I don't know what Jon is talking about here. I was, and still am, under the impression that Smithers took the car in without Jon's involvement. I can't say that definitively, as I was in California. But what I said to Jon – my "admission last night" (when we were rehashing this in the pool house) - was that I asked him (Jon) to help get my car to the shop *because* he had George – his assistant – who *could have* helped. (I never said Jon took my car, or any people, anywhere.) My understanding was that Smithers picked up the car from where I'd left it at Jon's house and brought it to the shop, on his own. And my impression was that Jon got irritated by Smithers doing it so willingly because he'd realized that saying "no" so adamantly in the first place had been a bit hasty, seeing as Smithers made the time to do it. But perhaps Jon did not have the a-ha moment I'd assumed he had when Smithers showed up looking for the keys. I may be missing some details given that I wasn't in town for any of this part. All I know with any certainty is that Jon said "no" and Smithers said "yes."

So to me, Smithers saved the day.

Jon called me in California, mad. As to why he was mad, you'd have to ask him. I told him, at the time, that he was mad because a friend of mine (who he wasn't particularly fond of) had been willing to do what he was not, and that made him look bad. I was just happy my car was fixed when I got back, and happy to have a friend who took the time to help me out, no questions asked.

Jon texted me to alert me that he'd sent the last email. I typed out this response email, sent it, then called him immediately. I knew that we'd be more likely to dig our hole deeper if he read and responded to this email, and that speaking on the phone gave us a better shot at settling things down rather than revving them up some more. I also didn't want to keep the emails going back-and-forth – we did enough of that during our relationship.

I responded at 2:22pm, with…(*this is 7+ years since we broke up…*):

Hey Jon ☺ I'm glad we can have these conversations around the impact and influence of our relationship & stuff, rather than just stuffing it under a rug. All I ever wanted in a partner was someone who inspired me to be a better person. While you were never going to be that, you did teach me a lot of useful things about the world and we had a lot of fun times together. We have insanely different values and the things that might matter to me may not matter to you, and being challenged to think about this stuff has been helpful.

I have no mean energy toward you - I really don't. I may be a little resentful of the amount of money I gambled away when we were together, given that I knew nothing about gambling when we met and the 90k my parents had invested that I blew through while we were together is gone…again, its about the influence you have…ya know?

I mean, I love that I won the very first poker tournament I was ever in…(well, a 10 way split win where I walked away with $3,500…but for someone in their early 20's that was a big deal!…) - I mean, that was great for my self esteem in the moment but if I just never got into gambling I'd be a lot better off…

So yeah, Jon, there are a lot of layers to the influence you have over others. Again, I'm not mad at you. If you can get over the pool house floor being discolored I can get over you chipping my tooth. Lol

(**Yes, I got extra digs in…I am not above being a brat sometimes. I included the money stuff because when I say "influence" I think Jon believes I'm referring to drugs, and that is only a piece of the influence pie I am speaking of. I called him after hitting send, because I didn't want to unsend it, but I did want to **bury hatchets…but..keep maps of where I put 'em…**)

*Suggested listen: **It's time to go…** -Taylor Swift

CHAPTER 40

• • • • • • ● • • • • • •

Right Where You Left Me

For a long time, I have been love-avoidant. I no longer trust myself to pick a partner – not after the Jon-then-Nathan-double-whammy. I even joke now that if *I'm* attracted to you, it probably means you're toxic as fuck. And, of course, as a mental health counselor who regularly works with couples who are struggling, I am reminded of reasons why even being in a healthy relationship can bring challenges that make me hesitate to try and find one for myself. For a long time now, I have been on board with hooking up and saying goodbye. Sure enough, if I start to see someone I hook up with as having the potential to become something more, the more they share about themselves, the more I prove my own theory, which is this: to me, toxic = hot. I'm guessing this is because I got so used to it and not because I *actually* think problematic people are sexier (…at least, I hope I don't.)

CHAPTER 41

•••••••••••••••

Enchanted to Meet You

In January of 2018, I was hanging out at my apartment with a (former boy) friend named Grant and another guy who had randomly come over from Grindr named Enrique, who was in his early 20s. We were all chatting, with Enrique deciding that the stripper pole in my living room provided him an opportunity to try something new. Clothing was optional at best for all three of us. Porn was playing on the TV. (*Perhaps some may find this set-up to be odd, but many gay men have been there, done that.*) I'd been messaging with an additional dude from Grindr who had recently moved to the area and appeared to be quite sexy from his pics. I invited him over, and he accepted the invitation.

William knocked and entered into the apartment when I was in the bathroom. He showed up, initially explaining that he'd been at a "family outing" earlier that evening. Enrique was naked on the stripper pole, Grant was on the couch – he'd put his underwear back on to answer the door - and I exited the bathroom and introduced myself, naked. Of course, William was fully clothed (as most are when they've just come from being around their family). He looked like Tom of Finland art I'd seen, with the masculine jawline, black hair, mustache, and all. William removed his shirt and sat on the sectional couch opposite Grant and me. We all got to chatting, with Enrique randomly spinning around the pole and interjecting commentary. William asked what we'd been up to that evening. We let him know that he was looking at it. Just chilling.

William shared, "I did blow tonight..." Grant and I questioned if he was *sure* he wasn't a cop – which makes sense, given that a great deal of Tom of Finland art *is* cops. He assured us he was not one, and so the party began.

William explained he'd recently moved from L.A. Grant and I were being chatterboxes. This guy was hella cute, and we wanted to know what he was all about. Grant kept interjecting ridiculous commentary. When William asked what meth was like, Grant replied that it was "like dick...some people *like* it...some LOVE it! Just like dick."

William: But what does it *feel* like?

Grant described it as feeling "awake...alive...ready to live!"

William inquired about where to buy beer nearby, so I let him know two gas stations were close by. But rather than make a move, he kept asking questions about local drugs... (*this is probably when we should have questioned if he was a cop. He is not, and so Grant just kept sharing...*)

William: Where do you get it? How much does it cost? Is it big here in Raleigh? Is it like weed?

Grant replied: "Weed is for fat people."

William: Does it wake you up?

Grant: "Yes!...HORNY!" I busted out laughing at this answer because William had not asked anything about libido.

William explained, "I feel like it has such a bad stigma..." He went on to say, "I've done everything except crack and heroin." I think it was *implied* that he also meant meth, given all of his questions. He also shared that he'd never *paid* for coke.

Meanwhile, Enrique just continues to swing around naked on the stripper pole.

William posed other questions, asking how Grant and I knew each other and if we liked going out (to bars and clubs).

Bruce: "I do, Grant doesn't…" I went on to share that I had gotten Grant to come out with me one time, and we'd had a lot of fun.

William asked what we did for work. Grant alluded to being a gigolo…but then admitted to being a hairstylist. Grant then went on a tangent about dudes on Grindr asking him if he's "generous" (think: sugar daddy). *Grant was deeply offended by the question, as he was 33. William shared that he was a photographer, to which I mentioned that I'd noticed he was very talented based on his Instagram page. (I got away with not responding to the question.)

William made a couple of comments that may've rubbed *sensitive* people the wrong way. He described the go-go boys at a local bar as "trash", reminding us, "I just came from L.A…"

William asked if I had any gym shorts, to which Grant interjected, "Get naked!"

William excused himself to go to the bathroom.

I asked Enrique, "Do you have class tomorrow?" Enrique confirmed that yes, he did, but he was planning to just stay awake until class. *Enrique was in college at a local university known for its engineering programs, but I have no idea what he was in school for.

I got up to go get William the gym shorts he'd asked for, noting he better watch out! My dogs may run out of the bedroom…William said no worries, he didn't need them after all.

Enrique asked William about his shoulder tattoo, to which William explained the meaning behind it. William then returned and sat down on the couch, letting us know he was cold. I inquire, "Do you want me to hold you?" William didn't skip a beat. "I will hold you…" going on to explain that would be his preference.

William asked where the porn was playing from? I handed him the iPad, and he asked if it 'had internet.' Grant asked William if he shoots porn for work? William was vague in his response…

William reverted to his drug-related questions, asking what snorting meth was like as he handed me the iPad. I inquired, "What kind of porn do you like?" William responded with, "What kind of porn do *you* like?" I simply stated anything that wasn't "gross" and that I was "pretty open-minded." William shared that he likes bi-porn...military...college...frat. "That's hot." William muttered something under his breath, to which I responded, "Wait...you're IN porn?!?!" William stated, "Yes", to which I inquired, "What's your porn name?" (I think he may've told me at this time, but he did not want it to be found, nor did he want it to be part of the first impression he was making.)

I continued to scroll through seancody.com, looking for a new video to put up on the TV. William stopped my scrolling and pointed to the iPad, noting, "I've met both of them, and they are sooo dumb." William then inquired if I had any Viagra. I let him know I did not, to which he said that was fine and that he didn't need it.

Enrique stammered somewhat aggressively, "WHAT DO YOU *WANT* TO DO!?"

William stated, "Photography." He went on to say, "I'm *already* doing *it*." I'm not sure if Enrique meant to come off as judgmental. And I don't know if he was offended by the idea of a career photographer or that William had been in porn. I came to William's defense, noting once again that William was very talented.

William and I were sitting side by side when he again noted that he was still cold. I let him know that "I have no problem cuddling you..." as I jumped up to turn the heat on for William.

William was back scrolling on the iPad when I asked, "You gonna show us your porn now? Did we *finally* break you down?.." William denies the request.

William says he wants to snort some meth. I let him know I wouldn't be doing it with him because it hurts too bad. But William still wants to do it...and so he does. After he did a line, he asked where I got my stripper pole, so I shared that info. William asks about the Wi-Fi password and then asks, "What do you have going on today?" To which Grant replies, "...this..." Grant then looks at Enrique and states, "*he's* got class."

Conversation resumes, and William states he needs some vodka. I tell him I don't have any alcohol but ask if he'd like some GHB instead... "GHB!? GHB is way too much for me..." William reverts to the topic of meth and inquires, "What does *it* look like?" and again asks where to buy it and how much does it cost in this area? I let him know that I don't know the answer to that question as I don't know any local dealers. William then states that coke in Raleigh is $100 per gram, to which Grant relays that "meth is about the same."

Enrique continues pole dancing, naked, but the rest of us are back in underwear

William asks: What're you guys doing this weekend?

Me: I don't know...I don't think I have any official plans...What are you up to?

W: I'm gonna be a V.I.P. for M.A.L...

Me: What is that?

W: You don't know what M.A.L. is?

Me: I probably will once you tell me what it stands for...

W. Mid Atlantic Leather Weekend?

Me: Oh! No, I didn't know what that was...

W: I'm photographing for it...

Then Grant wants the poppers. I'd given them to William when he initially asked for them, along with the glass of water he'd asked for, not long after his arrival. This was less than an hour later, and they were nowhere to be found...

We all four begin the scavenger hunt. "I have other bottles of poppers, but the ones we had out should be fine...and we just had them...?" We've got our camera phone flashlights out, turning over couch cushions, looking under the sofa skirt. Grant is looking everywhere, stating, "I *know* they have to be here."

Enrique pulls up a picture of himself on his phone where he has bleached hair. He shows it to Grant, who says, "Oh my god...but *where are the poppers!?*"

Grant and I were determined to find them, combing the floor and retracing our steps in my apartment living room, which was not particularly big. We are baffled.

William says, "They'll show up eventually." I note that the bottle "should be findable...we just had them..." Grant says, "Oh my god, where are the poppers!?"

William states, "They *really* disappeared." We continued looking for the MIA poppers bottle - which was one of the little ones and so could have easily rolled away somewhere, I figured. William notes, "They, like, evaporated..."

Then Enrique shows William his bleached hair pic. William asks a couple of questions about how difficult it had been to get his hair that light, given that he was standing in my living room (for Popper Gate 2018) and it was jet black. William also inquired how long it took to grow out back to 'normal.'

We wind down the search, and I go grab another bottle of poppers to share with the group. Enrique asks William, who has wrapped himself up in a blanket, "Are you disappointed in the type of people in Raleigh as opposed to LA?"

William: "No...I mean, LA is like the hub of entertainment, so of course there are a higher number of attractive people...but they're all vapid as fuck." I walk by William, and my foot touches his. "Oh my god, you're so cold," I remark. "It's fucking cold in here, man," he says. "I know I know, let me look at this..." I begin fiddling with the A/C settings. (No one else is cold, but I wasn't trying to be a rude host!) Then I squeeze in with William, noting, "Look, there are lots of blankets." Then I ask, "What part of you is freezing?" and he says, "Everything." "Do you want me to turn the heat on?" "yeah...aren't y'all cold?" "I mean, I'm not *that* cold, but I can turn the heat on..."

William and I are chit-chatting, cuddled up. I ask, "You want me to start a fire?" to which he replies, "You have a fireplace..." "I know, I do...say the word, and I'll do it." William then asks how old I am, and I tell him, "32."

"Nah, ah.." "Yep...Grant is 33..." William doesn't believe me on either statement – he was 25. "You don't look it at all." Grant comes back from the bathroom.

All four of us are seated at this point. William and I are sitting beside each other on the far-left side of the sectional, Enrique is on the other section, and Grant is on the loveseat.

William: Did y'all do anything else tonight? (Nope).

William: Were y'all looking for a party? (Nope).

William hits the new bottle of poppers I brought out, and I inquire, "Do poppers make you horny?" to which he replies, "Not really...I'm kind of asexual." Me: "Really!?" He says, "My favorite are uppers because I like to connect with people...and talk and chill, like this. It's cool. And sex is, like, 30 minutes out of your day..."

Grant: (baffled and disappointed) "*Sweet*..." (Grant and I laugh) Grant notes, "I'm just kidding..."

William: "I'll watch...if you guys wanna fuck...I don't care..."

Grant: "You know...we do *that* enough..." (laughs).

CHAPTER 42

•••••••• • •••••••

Grindr

We begin chatting about Grindr. I received a message on Grindr from Enrique asking if I had weed, along with a bunch of smoke emojis...we all received this message. He was sending out a bunch of messages to everyone around us in a 5-mile radius, desperate. He explains himself, and I say, "So you're sending *that* out to everybody? That's so crazy – don't be sending thousands of messages to everyone, asking if they want to smoke!..." All three of us come down on him. "Dude, don't do that..." Grant says. William just says, "Wow...we're gonna have to block that." Grant: Don't do that to everybody." *Enrique was young – he didn't know any better. Also, English is not his first language...*

Enrique: What? What're they gonna do, fucking *fight* me.

We all laugh...*fight you?*...what was he talking about?

Enrique: Right, I do know, but who knows if these people are crazy...

William: Don't just ask people for drugs...

Grant: Don't, like, *say* it...

William: A lot of people don't do drugs...

This leads to William explaining that at 2 am, he was up and wanted to see if anyone was "up like me...ya know, fucked up or whatever... and then sure enough...[I found you guys]. And I didn't have to message everybody in Raleigh."

Enrique: And see...that's like...I'm good at it...

Me: Yeah, but you also just showed me that you sent that message to 40 people...

Grant: Yeah, and then it's like, people like, what are you doing up so late? And I'm like, what-the-fuck-are-YOU-doing-up-so-late?!? (laughs) Are you high?? …Oh, you're gonna say that to ME? Like, god…*maybe* I'm a nurse at the hospital…I just started my shift…I'm like, stay-in-your-own-lane!…" (We are all laughing because Grant is *not* a nurse and is making fun of his own defensiveness.)

Me: Ya know, in the afternoon, they probably woulda just said, "What're you on here for?" and you wouldn't have gotten defensive, but then at night, they say something, and you're like, "What the fuck!?"

Then we talk about blocking people on Grindr vs. simply not replying to people. Enrique says he just doesn't reply to people he's not interested in, like, "Not interested…*don't* say I'm hot later…" whereas I say, "I block 'em…because if you don't, they just keep writing and writing, like "what're you up to now?" and I'm like, "I never wrote back the first time…so…"

Grant says (talking about me…), "I like the suspense, just waiting to see, like, did he unblock me yet? Did he unblock me?…" (…I did mention he's an ex-boyfriend, right?) laughs. "I'm kidding…"

Grant: I wish people would be more like me…(*laughs). (Me: In what way?) Well, you know, like, the ones that say, "Have a picture on your profile if you're gonna ask for it…" and I'm like, "YOU don't have a picture on YOUR profile!…"

Enrique: What about a body pic?

Grant: If it's *theirs*…*(laughs)*…you know, how many people have, like…Bruce, you remember…that one dude out there, that like, got my photos…and you were like, "you got another profile out there?…"

Me: Oh yeah!! This guy that was here that I hung out with - he was cute too!

William: He stole your photos!

Grant: I gave him ALL my photos!…

William: He stole ALL your photos!

Me: He and I hung out. He was pretty cool…I saved him to my favorites…and then *his* photo switched to Grant's photo…and I was like, I know HIM!? Like, what the fuck..?

*So what happened was that Grant's face showed up twice in my favorites, one that was Grant and one that was the photo thief. What I never got around to saying in this conversation was that this dude – who was fucking hot – and I went to hook up with this other dude I'd fucked before (but didn't remember I had until we got there…). Anyway, just like the first time this dude was naked, F.D.A.U. if you know what I'm talkin' about. We both fucked him some and then this hottie started fisting him. This was the first time I'd witnessed this. And it was bananas. While hanging out with the hottie, he'd mentioned he was in the military and would be heading back to base when the weekend ended. Little did I know at some point he chatted up Grant, stole his pics, and swapped them with his own, I guess, once he was back on base. But all I knew was that suddenly Grant had two profiles – one in town and one further away. I asked Grant about it via text message before I opened up the profiles and realized this was the fisting photo thief and military hottie. *

Grant (explaining to William): And then Bruce texted me, like, "So you're out of town?" And I'm like, "Fuck no, I'm at my apartment…" And he's like, "Nah ah…"

Me: Then I open it up, and I'm like, wait, this is the *conversation* I had with that other guy…but Grant's face…

Grant: He totally led me on the whole time, and he literally got ALL my pictures…and then he started using my fuckin' photos…

Me: He wanted to be you… (joking)

William: You gotta be careful who you trust on Grindr, though…you gotta see the signs…

Me: …he's in the military too…but I don't think that's an excuse.

Grant: Yeah, It's not.

William: It's really not, though.

Grant: It's like c'mon dude. Do we know that you're in the military? No! ...Does it matter? I mean, you're on Grindr, c'mon.

Then I blew William a shotgun, which led to us making out for a good 20 seconds. *I did not see that coming.*

We got to chatting again. William inquired, "There's not a bathhouse in Raleigh, is there?" I responded, "There's not, no...but we can open one!"

This led to a discussion of bathhouses, video stores and the Raleigh laws that (apparently) don't allow for such an establishment here. Grant speaks of the various Raleigh establishments that allow for hook-ups, including one location that's "the nice one...you have to pay $10", where "they've got rooms with futons..." vs. the other one, where they have "murder booths."

William notes, "I haven't been to one here, but I like the one in Paris." Grant reacts to this, stating that "if you're used to Paris and LA, and that shit...in Raleigh...we're gonna, like, not get along..." (laughs).

William: I mean I...I don't think so...

Grant: Well...ok.

CHAPTER 43

·········· ● ●● ● ● ·········

Poppers Found!

Enrique: What'd you like about Raleigh?

William: I was born here…

Me: Oh, you were!?

William: My family's here, that's about it. I like one bar here called Ruby Deluxe. It's, like, a very alternative bar where they play good music, I guess…

Me: What kinda music is good for you?

William: For me?…They play, like, very alternative, like, rock, and electronic, and rap…

As William is answering that question, Grant comes over and blows me a shotgun. From there, William and I confirm that we both love dancing when we go out. William talks about Ruby Deluxe's struggle to get people to come to their bar and how he hopes to help.

William asked questions about where I was from, how I ended up in Raleigh, and how long I'd been living here. Then Grant reappeared, asking William if he was warm. When William confirmed he still was not, Grant handed him a little bottle and said, "Here, poppers make you warmer." Grant went on to say, "I wanna find the *other* bottle…"

We all start hitting the poppers and passing them around. Then Grant exclaims, "Oh my god it's in the drink!" Sure enough, the missing poppers had somehow landed in William's glass of water.

I have never seen three people get so excited about finding a bottle of poppers. And I say three because Enrique was being very quiet.

Grant: Have you seen that popper porn?

We go back to chatting and chatting and chatting…

CHAPTER 44

· · · · · · · ● · · · · · ·

Question...?

William poses a question - when was your first experience with a man? – and then says, "I'm trying to get to know you guys..." So we start sharing our answers...

I overshare – telling an abbreviated version of the first time, followed by the first *enjoyable* time. And then I go on to talk about my first (and only) time having sex with a girl, too. (Yuck.)

William shared his first time with a man as well, noting that in high school, he'd bragged to his peers about girls he slept with as a front, but he'd known he was gay. William's first time with a man was also a bad time. So, I felt better about my bad first time – (which was only a bad time because I wasn't attracted to the guy when I was sober and didn't want to go to college a virgin) - and was glad to hear William's second time, like my own, had been better.

Grant tried to get out of sharing, but I called him out for it. "Have I not shared..?.." Grant was playing dumb. I made a joke (as if telling Grant's story...): "I was 8...the guy was 11..." Grant was evasive as hell, trying to get away with just saying, "I was 17..." and leaving it at that. But I learned that Grant started college at 17, and that's when it happened. Same age as me. And Grant went on to share the rest of it, too.

We all discussed what it was like realizing you were 'different' during various experiences, like when William was in Boy Scouts and did not realize what he was *feeling*. He recalled he was just eight years old.

139

Enrique shared, "I've never been fucked in my whole life."

William: Wait, what!?!? (*this boy had been naked and spinning around the pole for what seemed like hours.)

Me: Yep, and he's only topped, like, twice.

Enrique: Four times!

And that was the extent of what we learned about Enrique's first time.

Conversations about porn, sex, and drugs continued.

William shared: My favorite drug is ketamine. (*I knew I loved this man)

Then we discussed the difference between doing ketamine at a nightclub, vs. when you're aiming for a k-hole.

Then we just all lay back on the couch and watch porn. The light conversation continues.

William: It's time for the next question: What's your favorite position?

I answer thoroughly...but then we get distracted by the porn we're watching...and no one else gives their answer...

*The porn had an older dude with a young guy...

William: All of my boyfriends have been older than me...like, a lot older. (Pause...) My last serious boyfriend was fucking crazy. (I laugh loudly. Because: *Sidebar: Grant's last boyfriend threatened to slit my throat. The one time he ever called me, he called to say he wanted to end my life. So, when William says HIS last boyfriend was crazy, I'm immediately, like...**lookin' at you, G-money**...*) (Grant doesn't like where this conversation is headed...)

I asked William, "How long were you with him?"

But then Grant starts making the No-We-Are-Not-Falling-Down-This-Rabbit-Hole noise and hand gesture...and we avert the crisis that could have been: Ex-Boyfriend Roasting Time.

Grant re-focuses our attention on the porn.

William: I worked for a porn studio...I like, did camera work for a porn studio...

Me: Was it cool? I hear that, like, as the porn is being shot, it's actually *pretty terrible* for the actors.

William: Yeah, a lot of stop-and-go….I don't wanna ruin it for you, though…

Me: No, you're not…That's what I've heard. And I've actually heard that from multiple porn stars…

(**What the fuck am I talking about? I know *people* who have been in porn, yes…but porn stars? Multiple…? *WHAT*??** Lmfao. *Watching a Jenna Jameson documentary does not qualify me to make such a strong statement.)

William: I'd rather make a hot, homemade video and make a fourth of the money…

…but…I [knew I] would get paid, like, 5 grand if I came, so [I did it]…

Enrique: So…'camera work' is like, jerking off?

William: What?

Enrique: So 'camera work,' you're like jerking off?

William: Wait…wuddya mean..?

Enrique: Like, jerking off, that's a 'camera worker'…

Me: No no no no no no…not at all.

William: Like, I was doing…they offered me a position holding the camera. (Oh!) Yeah, like, being the photographer on set. Doing production assisting. Cleaning the set, making a set. Transporting the models, making sure they're fed. Basically, I learned how to do everything in the porn world. But I hated it in the end.

Me: Well, that's why you need to start a company here in Raleigh…do it on your own terms!

William: No. (chuckle)

Grant: Do it!……

…I am. (Grant laughs)

CHAPTER 45

•••••••• • •••••••

What's Your Fantasy?

William: I can start a bathhouse...If this was how it really is, I'd be Mormon in a hot minute...We should try this...let's go to...what is it? Let's go to Mormon class tomorrow... (*If you're gay, I'll bet you can guess what porn we're watching...)

Me: What if we get in there, and it's nothing like this?

William: We'd be so disappointed...Like, I'm gonna burn this place down...

Me: Yeah! Start playing this porn in church, like, what is happening... Nah, I'm just kidding.

William: I'm gonna make y'all my wives. And we can start a clan...

Me: We're not gonna have kids...

William: I don't care. I don't need a kid. Y'all are my sons.

Grant: Oh god...Father...

Me: Oh yeah? You're gonna be an elder?

William: So we're gonna start a farm. We're gonna, like, have a bunch of crops..

Me: I'll totally tend the fields as long as you're fucking us...

William: What?

Me: As long as you're gonna fuck us, Sir.

William: Well, I was getting to that. We'll have, like, fun little orgy tree houses in the fields.

Me: (laughs) I like the orgy tree houses.

William: I'm very imaginative.

Me: I mean, like, I'd sign up.

William: Okay, you're my first subscriber.

Me: Does that mean we're gonna fuck the most? If all these other people sign on behind us..?

William: The most?

Me: Oh, wait! It's an *orgy*…

*chit chat continues for a minute…then William announces:

William: Ok, so I have another **question…??** This is gonna be, like, a 21-question night. (some push-back…) Oh, I have *tons* of questions…But I need you guys to participate more. (Me: More than what?) Because in the past three hours, you guys…(William trails off…then asks…) What is your ultimate fantasy?

Enrique: I wanna have sex with a celebrity.

William: That's nothing. Celebrities are boring.

Grant: Bruce was it, today, baby!

Me: Shut the fuck up! (*laughing*)

William: Who?

Grant: Him! I walked in today, and he had the ball gag in his mouth. Fuck yeah!

Me: Shut the fuck up!

William: You're a freak!...

 Me: Yeah…

William: Are you really?

Me: Yeah, hell yeah.

William: That's hot.

Grant: I wanna have sex in public – the whole public shit.

William: You're a voyeur?...

Grant: Well yeah…I like sex inside, too…but…

Me: Wait, a voyeur is someone who *watches*, right??...

William: Do you guys go to gay parties?.... You've been on a cruise, right?

Me: Yeah, I've been on a cruise.

Grant: Yeah…it's A LOT.

William: Yeah, there's no "out."

143

*Grant made it sound like jealousy was a big part of his cruise experience – then he was stuck on a boat with whoever was getting jealous...

Me: I like the thought of getting fucked in a sling by the person I'm dating, but while a lot of other people watch.

William asked Enrique if he had anything to share (other than his first answer, which was rejected...)

Enrique: I actually wanna get in a relationship.

Me: I thought you just broke up with somebody, like, today?

William: *Today?*

Grant: Or...yesterday...(laughs)

Enrique: In the last two months. He didn't fuck me, though.

William: He didn't fuck you?

Me: Did you want him to?

William: That is so hot – when you get in a relationship and you get fucked. And the person *cares* about you.

Me: So true.

William: It's so much better...(yep!)...Like, "THIS isn't empty and meaningless!..."

Me: Right? (laughs) And you can fuck all the time and love it, and not...

William: (To Enrique) No, you'll find somebody, though. If that's what you want. Maybe not in Raleigh. You've got to graduate, and you can figure out what you like. Get confident...explore...that'd be my advice for you or for any young people. Like, figure out what you like first before you settle down. So many people jump into a relationship before they know what they like. I think it's sexy when a guy knows what he wants.

Enrique: Well, how do you...?

William: You have to explore. Fuck around. Sometimes, it looks like being a ho...or being a freak. But, like, go to parties and have sex and figure out what you like...

(*I make a comment under my breath*) Not in Raleigh, girl! M.A.L. this weekend!

    Me: Yeah, that does sound hot as hell…

    [*chit chat continues for a while]

    William asks Grant how he can get a haircut, and they talk about that for a while, then William goes to the restroom.

    Grant and I are chatting.

    I start talking about this guy who I drove out to "the middle of nowhere" to go hang out with "who wanted to fuck, like, all over his property…in the weeds, in the dirt. He was pretty hot, too. I was like, people-can-see-us…the neighbor's yards. I was like, what if your neighbors see you getting fucked, like? You have to live next to these people forever. I was having all these, like, paranoid thoughts, and he was like, "It's whatever.""

    William returned from the bathroom.

    Enrique inquired, "Are you going to get another tattoo?

    William: Uh huh…

    Me: Are you gonna get my face on your ass cheek? Actually, if my dick's on your ass cheek, I'd really appreciate it.

    William: Your face?

    Me: Yeah, would you mind?

    William: Like a Greek god?

    Me: Yeah, there you go…beautiful.

CHAPTER 46

•••••••• • ••••••••

We Were Lying On Your Couch, I Remember

Enrique was back on the pole.

When William returned from the restroom, he began complaining again about being cold. He asked me, "Do you *have* heat?" I told him I'd go turn on the dryer for him to warm the place up. He said, "Start a fire." Grant commented, "My mouth is warm…" William just said, "Good." He got under blankets on the corner of the couch I was sitting near. I got under them with him.

William started asking me questions about my last name and other stuff. Enrique was on the far end of the sectional. Grant was on the other. And William and I were in the corner…making out. We got lost in our own little world for a while. And all conversation stopped, as Enrique and Grant hadn't figured out how to talk to each other, I guess. At one point, Enrique came and sat down right next to us as we were making out. He was just watching us, with Grant on the other side of him. Awkward. But we didn't stop.

While we didn't have sex, we went further than we should have, given that there were spectators. Grant and Enrique must have been on the same wavelength – a mutual friend zone situation. Because they just looked at us as we were making out but made no moves for each other. One at a time, they got off the couch and moved…somewhere? I was doing exactly what I wanted to be doing and couldn't be bothered to be more inclusive. William and I were on the same wavelength, also.

I got up off the couch for a minute and stood up. Since there was the break-in-the-action, Grant walked over…

Grant: Do you want me to leave? I could, like, leave…

Me: Why? You don't have to leave. (*wrong answer!* – I thought I was being polite in this knee-jerk response, but I didn't want to hook up with Grant or Enrique anymore in this moment than they wanted to watch us but not participate. Stupid, stupid, stupid.)

I don't think I realized that Grant and Enrique couldn't entertain themselves…or that I was being a bad host. However you look at it, I should have let Grant go in this moment and hoped Enrique would follow his lead. I think I even admitted, "I forgot y'all were here," and apologized. But I said, "Y'all can go if we're making you uncomfortable…" Grant replied that no, he wanted to join…

William had already established that he did not bottom. Grant is a greedy bottom. Both Grant and I are vers, but I was not about to bring him in the mix when I didn't get the impression that William was into him and, more importantly, when I could be giving up the dick I was about to land.

This is when William put me on all fours and started eating my ass. And both spectators had taken their seats back on the couch, watching. Enrique was so close to us without attempting to get involved that it was just odd. Thinking about it now, I can't even be irritated with Grant – he read the room, said he could go, and my dumb ass said he didn't have to. And so, the stage was set to have some phenomenal sex.

William and I go back to making out for a minute, with me laying on top of William as we do it. Then I go to suck his dick. This left my ass up in the air. Grant leaped into action, thinking this was the ticket to get involved. I knew what he was up to, so I begrudgingly made a judgment call in that moment. "It's rude of us to be hooking

147

up...maybe we should stop...". I realized that if and when William and I slept together, I just wanted it to be the two of us. Somehow, I had caught feelings for this guy in a matter of hours. And I realized **I don't wanna look at anything else now that I saw you, and I don't wanna think of anything else now that I thought of you. -Daylight**, Taylor Swift

I get up and start showing off on the stripper pole. I have too much pent-up sexual energy not to, plus William is still on the couch, and I know I can't go back over there right now...

William and Enrique start chatting on the couch for a minute, and Enrique relays his academic struggles. "Push through, dude," is all William says. Then William gets up and shows off his moves.

It's hella fun having a stripper pole in your living room.

CHAPTER 47

•••••••• • ••••••••

One, two, three, not only you and me

The break we took from hooking up lasted about twenty minutes. William and I had resumed our close, cuddled-up conversation on the couch. He was showing me things on his phone for about five minutes before I started sucking his dick...for a long time. About four minutes into me sucking William's dick, Grant comes over, and William starts sucking Grant's dick. William is rock-hard. While I'm sucking William's dick, Grant makes a comment, "You've got two bottoms trying to get your dick," and I let it be known it's mine. Grant can play with it, too, but I've got first dibs...

William goes over to the bathroom, where Enrique has been holed up for a while. He bangs on it and asks, "Are you okay?" It's unclear if he said he'd thrown up or what was going on...but he says he's okay. Not long after that, Enrique exits the bathroom.

William says, "Hey buddy, do you mind heading out? Cuz we're about to...."

Enrique agreed to leave and began putting his clothes back on and collecting his things.

Enrique states, "I *might* wanna bottom today." We all let him know that he should not go on a search for dick and that he should not go cruising with strangers just to get his cherry popped. William reinforces, "We are looking out for your best interest." Enrique goes, and we are all happy with that development. As abrupt as William had been with asking him to go, I thought his assertiveness was incredibly sexy.

As Enrique is walking out, I'm sitting on William's dick. "How did he get here, anyway?" Wilson inquired. Grant and I explained that we'd found him on Grindr and that he'd only sent one pic. No one was commenting on his looks – he was attractive. It was more the things that came out of his mouth that confused us.

We began recapping to William some of the things he had said before William arrived, with William relaying that he felt just as uncomfortable with his close proximity as we were hooking up as I had been. I informed Grant that the dude had been hitting on him from the minute he got there – which stemmed from the conversation we'd all had before William arrived, where Enrique had informed us that Grant was a "9.5" and I was an "8.9." (It's still a running joke Grant and I have to this day, and it comes in handy whenever I need to remind Grant of his greatness.)

We stopped hooking up for a minute because William was cold again, and he asked me to lay on top of him. So I did. Then when Grant walked away to refill his water bottle, William started fucking me again. And Grant returned, seemingly out of place again. But he stood there, jacking off, while I started backwards cowboying William…Then Grant started sucking my dick. This was short-lived, but a fun time. Then I laid back down next to William and he began showing me photos on his phone. He **told me 'bout** his **past, thinkin'** his **future was me.**

Looking back on it now, there was no way for me not to develop feelings for William. He essentially came over to my place, sexy as hell, and he seemed to pick me over the other two dudes that were there. We had chemistry, and he was more interesting than anyone else I'd met recently. He had been places, and so had I. He had done things, and so had I. And he knew about things that I knew nothing about, and they sounded like fun things to do or to experience. I knew this was either the beginning of a romantic situation or, at the very least, a great friendship. They say people come into your life for a reason, a season, or a lifetime. And while

CLOSURE

William was only in my life for a season (over a year...but still...), things started out pretty great between us. They also say people in your life are either a lesson or a blessin'. He started as a blessing but ultimately taught me a lot of important lessons. So perhaps he's both? ...**sometimes I wonder how you think about it now...**I'd imagine I left him with a net negative. But I'm getting ahead of myself...

CHAPTER 48

•••••••• • •••••••

The Very First Night

I made some major mistakes the night I met William if I wanted to date him. First of all, I didn't kick the duo out when I should have. Second thing – I knew I wanted to date William after just hanging out for a few hours…We'll call it a **'daylight** moment'. But for whatever reason, I still let Grant fuck me in front of William because I didn't want to be **mean**. Which probably wasn't that big of a deal…but Grant and I had fucked plenty, and so it maybe appeared to William I enjoyed it more (?). I'm just speculating. But I knew once I saw William, I didn't want to look at, think of, or be with anyone else. I, personally, don't get off watching a partner of mine *be* with someone else. And while William and I hadn't locked anything down officially, I wouldn't have wanted to see him with Grant…or anyone else…

It was around this time that we were all three laid back on the couch when William finally showed us the porn he'd been in. Oddly enough, he bottoms in most of the videos. It makes me wonder if that experience is why he said at the time we met him he was a "top only", or if that had nothing to do with it. But who knows…He also said he was asexual.

His porn is very real, and while he's not the first porn actor I've ever known personally, he is the person whose porn I can find the most easily on the internet. Partly because I know his porn name and partly because there's a lot of it. It's weird to watch it, given that he's a much more intricate person than these videos suggest. But I'd imagine all porn actors are, right? **He was wild 'n crazy, just so**

frustrating, intoxicating, complicated, got away, my sole mistake and now...

    The night wrapped up, finally, after I began falling asleep on my couch. I have no idea if Grant and William went somewhere together or parted ways. I was so tired I just passed out. Grant later told me he was jealous that William and I were clearly into each other and felt excluded. It was nice to have confirmation that this wasn't all in my head...especially since Grant is a 9.5.

CHAPTER 49

•••••• • ••••••

It's Nice to Have a Friend

Did I mention that William shared at some point early on that he was working as an escort? No judgment – he had to do what he had to do to make ends meet. I remember sending him a screenshot alerting him that his profile on Rentmen.com had his dad's exact address set as his location. (Most other escorts simply had "Raleigh" as their location, so I felt like this was useful information for him to have. And he fixed it.)

William and I hung out pretty regularly over the next month. We did standard friend things together. Occasionally, we would hook up, but plenty of times, we hung out, and it was strictly platonic.

About 20 days after we'd initially met, we were hanging out. We went to a porn-and-sex-toy shop because we were bored. We bought a few gay XXX magazines because William had a brilliant idea: we were going to make a collage on a canvas. He was a creative person, being a photographer and all. And he knew I had a creative side – I had melted crayons on my apartment walls...and on canvasses...to brighten the place up. So once we'd purchased our magazines, we headed back to my place. I had a canvass, so we got to work.

We put together an awesome collection of sexual words, naked men, and other brilliantly placed items to perfect our artwork. We meticulously set the pieces we'd clipped from the magazines onto the canvas, so all the white space was covered. We didn't have any glue or lacquer, but we had gotten all of the pieces exactly where we wanted them. And our masterpiece was essentially complete. We needed to put it somewhere it wouldn't be disturbed until we got the lacquer necessary to lock all of the pieces exactly where we wanted them, so I put the canvas on top of a tall dresser in my living room to be sure my dogs couldn't mess with it. It was perfect.

William and I laid back on the couch. I put my head on his chest as we were cuddling. He started rubbing my thigh, then my butt. We were chatting, and I was happy. I couldn't figure out why this incredibly attractive dude liked hanging out with me. My head felt right on his chest. I didn't actually give a shit that he was an escort – if anything, I liked that he'd chosen to spend time with me when other dudes had to pay for it. This guy gave me butterflies...those stupid fucking butterflies...He put his arm around me and pulled me in close, rubbing my upper arm...

Me: Oh, fuck!

William: Oh my God, that's so funny!

Me: I did not even think of that...oh my god, that's soo stupid of me!...ahh, that's so ridiculous!... (William is laughing). That's so stupid, I'm such a fucking idiot....Oh my god, that really just happened...

The air conditioning unit had kicked on, and the vent blew all of our collage pieces right off the canvas, so there was gay porn confetti falling from the sky. It was absolutely ridiculous. But also, fucking hilarious. William hugged my head as I was beating myself up. He just laughed.

Both of my dogs were jumping on my face because they knew something exciting was going on, but they didn't know what...

William commented, "I wish I had that on video."

Me: There's pictures of naked people everywhere...

William: "Bruce..."

I was commenting on what an airhead I was for putting our masterpiece up there in the first place. William was laughing as I walked over to where the pieces had landed and commented, "That's just so fucking dumb..."

William: I'm going to document this…

William grabbed his phone and started shooting a video. "Me and Bruce were just doing arts and crafts for that canvas up there, and we put a pause on it because we got so far into it…all the pictures laid out beautifully on the canvas, and we stuck it up there…and the vent turned on and all the pictures went EVERYWHERE…that's hilarious."

Me: That did not even cross my mind…well… However they get laid out next time will be even better. They looked pretty good, the way we had it…but you can't live in the past, right?

William and I picked up the clippings from all over the floor. I kept commenting on my stupidity. "If I only had a brain…"

He was in his underwear and a sweatshirt. I was in jeans and a Polo shirt. I am glad this turn of events didn't interrupt our otherwise scheduled program…

We laid back down on the couch and started hooking up…It was nice to have sex with him without anyone else around. He was awesome.

CHAPTER 50

•••••••• • •••••••

Another Chipped Tooth

A friend of mine brews her own beer. Stupid me, I don't even like beer all that much. Which made me a poor judge when it came to estimating how much I could drink and still be 'normal.'

William and I had plans to go out to Legends one evening early on in our friendship. The plan was to meet at my apartment and go from there.

I'd been over at my friend's house who home brews for the first time, just hanging out and seeing what all that process entailed. Meanwhile, she's handing me abnormally big beer bottles and suggesting I see what I like. There's an outside brewing situation involving an open flame...we've got big ass pots on the stove...there's some huge sacks of grain involved. I don't know what I can do to be helpful, but if I'm told to do it, I help. All the while sipping on these oversized bottles of beer. I tell my friend, Jerri, who's all into this brewing-of-beer situation about this new boy in my life that I'm into. I let her know that I have to leave at a certain time so I can meet him at my apartment, and we can go out tonight. She's happy for me – she is in a relationship and is happy, so she wishes me the same **happiness**. And although she's still brewing up a storm as I leave, she understands when I say I must go. She sent me away with some unopened bottles of home-brewed beer, and off I went.

It wasn't until I was back at my apartment that it dawned on me that I was much more drunk than I'd even realized. It was still daylight when I left Jerri's place, and I was not typically intoxicated when it was still daylight...ever.

And the best-but-worst part was that William was already on his way over. Which was great – I was excited to see him! But was terrible because I am not a day-drunk kinda guy...I felt like I could hold it together just fine, though. After all, I had managed to drive home just fine, and I had not opened any of the beers Jerri had sent me home with.

William, being the sweet guy that he was, showed up at my apartment with a bottle of wine. How thoughtful! Stupidly, I dropped the unopened bottle onto the kitchen floor while holding it by the neck. It just slipped from my fingers and shattered everywhere.

Fortunately, William was not mad. Which was nice – I could have easily seen someone getting irritated by this turn of events.

Unfortunately, when William was sitting on the loveseat in my living room, he spotted the poppers on the counter. He asked if he could use them, so I picked up the little glass bottle and underhand-tossed them his way. What I hadn't realized was just how invested he was in looking at his phone, and the bottle managed to land on his face – or, more specifically, on one of his teeth. And yes, that tooth had chipped. While it was a very subtle chip, it was a chip nonetheless. And William had teeth that were just about perfect before this event.

I profusely apologized for what had happened. He took a minute to look in the mirror to confirm that, sure enough, he could tell that a little piece was missing. I immediately offered to pay whatever the dental bill was going to be. He let me know he didn't have insurance – to which I responded that I would pay it no matter what the cost. I think I even told him that I knew what it was like to have your tooth chipped by someone else, and the very least I could do was pay for it.

He acted like he wasn't mad about the situation while also letting me know that he was going to go...he was no longer feeling like going out to a club this evening. He was just going to head home to his dad's house. He let me know that he wasn't mad. He just wasn't feeling it. And so William left. I was sad. But also drunk, and totally understanding of why he chose to leave. I briefly questioned if I had ruined something that had the potential to be great. I figured if that was the case, I had no one to blame but myself.

I mentioned that it was still daylight out when I got back to my place, which meant I had plenty of time to sober up before I went out to the club later that evening. I think I even took a nap – after all, sometimes sleep is your best option when you realize being awake only makes things worse. But once I woke up and was sober, I still wanted to go out. And so I got changed and headed downtown.

What I hadn't anticipated was that William might also have decided that the bar was where he wanted to be that evening, and not back at his dad's house for the evening. Just because he'd recently moved back to the area, it didn't mean he couldn't go out and make new friends. I only caught a glimpse of him when I was out on the dance floor, but that was all I needed to switch into crazy mode. I have no idea what I texted him that evening, but I know that it was some combo-pack of profuse apologies for what had happened as well as irritation that he'd gone out when he said he was going home. I had no right to be possessive, and yet I knew that I wanted to be the person he was dancing with and paying attention to that evening…and I was supposed to be! But I'd fucked it all up. If I remember correctly; it wasn't even until I got home that evening that I texted him. It was just one long paragraph that he never responded to…

Suggested listen: **Hits Different** -Taylor Swift

CHAPTER 51

•••••••• • •••••••

I think there's been a glitch

I was not willing to settle for a non-response. My apology texts may not have gone through, but I was pretty sure he'd gotten the ones I sent through Facebook messenger. But no response ever came. William had mentioned that the one bar in town that he liked was Ruby Deluxe. So I knew what I had to do…

Ruby had some kind of theme night – I think it was leather night – coming up soon. I dressed the part – I wasn't about to show up in regular clothes. Plus, it allowed me to walk up on William without him seeing me coming – thanks to a leather mask for my lower face. My reason for tracking him down? – I needed this man to know how sorry I was for all of it. And if he wanted to spit in my face, I was down for that. Or if he had a dental bill for me, that was cool, too. I just wanted him to know I knew I'd fucked up. I was obviously still crushing on him, but also guilt-ridden. And I couldn't let it go…

How I figured out he was going to be there, I cannot remember. But I do remember being relatively confident he would be…and I was right. He was standing out on the patio, and I pretty much made him talk to me. When he saw my face, I could tell he wanted anyone but me to be in front of him. If eyes could incinerate, I would not be here today.

While looking over my shoulder the entire time we spoke, he assured me we were fine. He may not have been able to make eye contact with me, but hearing that from his mouth was better than not hearing anything from him ever again, so I took it. And so I stuck around at the bar.

CLOSURE

Eventually, his face softened, and he didn't look like he wanted to punch me any longer. He even introduced me to a person or two, one of whom was a coke dealer and friend of his. William had no problem making friends. And he'd already mentioned that he wanted this bar to succeed, which must be how I figured he'd be here that night. I was just glad he was being relatively nice. And glad that we were able to recover a friendship.

CHAPTER 52

•••••••• • •••••••

The Fruit

William and I hung out quite a bit over the following months. I used to leave a key for him outside of my apartment in case he needed a place to meet clients. My apartment was nothing to brag about, but since he was living at his dad's, I figured he couldn't have in-calls, and that may have been a necessary part of the job. I have no idea if he ever used my place for this purpose, but I do know he hung out there a little when I was at work.

William's claim to fame was photographing nude guys artistically. And he was (and is) very talented. So when William would ask about my day, I typically had a pretty routine answer, as being a therapist at a college counseling center isn't dramatically different from day-to-day. Not to mention the confidentiality piece, so "it was pretty good. Same-old-same-old" was a fairly standard response from me. William, on the other hand, would tell of photo shoots with guys he'd recruited to model. And of clients he'd met up with for other purposes, although he'd typically be more secretive about these specifics. He wouldn't name names or provide identifying info, but I was told enough to know that business was good.

We would go out on the weekends to Ruby Deluxe or Legends. All the while, I was crushing on him, with the knowledge that I'd done a solid job of proving myself to be far too chaotic to be this man's partner. William in no way led me on — after I managed to get his forgiveness and recover the friendship, there was no ambiguity from him around where we stood. I'd been friend-zoned permanently, and I knew exactly why. I just had to make peace with it. I tried to talk to him at Legends one time about the feelings I had for him…he responded by telling me he'd been in Durham earlier that day, had stopped to eat at a Mexican restaurant, and he ended up fucking his waiter. He wasn't a complete dick about it, but I probably needed the tough love in order to fully embrace the idea that we were just meant to be friends.

It seemed that William would tell someone he wanted to photograph them everywhere we went. He was quite the hustler, I guess, literally and figuratively. He was also super-charming and very handsome, so it was no surprise that some of these people took him up on his offer. Occasionally, he would tell me about an upcoming trip that someone was flying him in for or a photography gig he'd booked out of town. Sometimes, he would disappear for the few days that aligned with the trip he'd been telling me about, but oftentimes, these trips seemed to fall through. I think most of the ones that fell through were escorting gigs, but I'm not completely sure. William had a way of telling me some of the information while remaining allusive, always headed to stay on a friend's couch *here* or spend a few days shooting photos *there*. I remember one time William called me because he'd left my apartment to go to a booking with a new client, but when he got to the hotel, he said there was a police car parked in the parking lot with its lights on, so he got spooked and canceled the appointment. I guess you can never be too careful – sex work is still illegal in North Carolina.

William was genuinely invested in using his engaging personality and/or photography skills to promote places he felt needed help getting the word out. Ruby Deluxe was one such place. The Durham Fruit Company was another. William got to know some of the local DJs who spun at The Fruit and would tell anyone who liked dancing in rave-style warehouses about upcoming shows. The Fruit is a tremendous place when they open up all of the building, and they can have three DJs spinning at the same time and not have anyone's musical toes get stepped on. It's two stories and always a really fun time.

I was used to William sharing about hot dudes he'd photographed or clients he'd 'spent time' with and had found a way of compartmentalizing any lingering feelings I had for him. Plus, when you're friends with someone you may've initially had a crush on, I've found that in most cases, you can start to see why it never would have worked out in the long run, anyway. (*Most*...but not all...) I certainly never held it against him that he was a sex worker, but if he'd been my boyfriend, I have no doubt this would have become majorly problematic at some point. And let's not forget: If I'm looking at things from his perspective, I was throwing up red flag after red flag after red flag from the start...hell, even the fact that I showed up at Ruby Deluxe to make him talk to me, in retrospect, would be a red flag! But somehow, we'd talked through a lot and were making the friendship work.

I knew it meant *something* when, in July of 2018, William mentioned there was a guy, Ryan, who he really wanted me to meet. William just knew something was *different* about Ryan...This was a big deal, in that William had told me about plenty of dudes, but never one that he had real *feelings* for. And he phrased it in such a way that made me feel as though I had some kind of wisdom to discern if this guy was actually as great as William believed he was or not. William shared a very short pros and cons list with me: Pro – he's great in bed. Con – he's a restaurant manager. I personally did not understand why that was a con...but okay. *I think gay people (and maybe all people...?) can be hyper-judgmental about other people's careers, but if what you do makes you happy and/or pays the bills, then who's to say what is and is not acceptable? Oh, also, it was made explicitly clear that when I met this man, I was to make NO mention – ever – of any escort-related shenanigans. After all, you can only judge someone for what you know – not what you don't...right?

But dishonesty is never the best policy.

CLOSURE

On July 20th, I met Ryan for the first time. William, Ryan, me, and my friend Skyler were all headed to The Durham Fruit Company for a Saturday night rave-style dance party. And I'd been tasked with multiple jobs that evening by William. First and foremost, I was to assess whether or not Ryan was awesome-sauce or not. Secondly, once we got to the venue, I was expected to confuse any situation that made it seem as though William was tied down to any one specific dude. Because William had invited many people to the show, and had suggested to at least three guys that they stood a fair shot at going home with him that evening. This was how William presented things despite telling me in confidence that he intended on making sure Ryan knew he was number one. I have no idea how William wound up in this situation or why he thought this was going to run smoothly, but he was optimistic he could pull it off.

So the evening started like this: Skyler showed up first to my apartment, and William and Ryan were not far behind. I got to meet Ryan briefly before we all loaded up in the car. He seemed cool.

A good time was bound to be had by all. And so we packed into William's car – William in the driver's seat, Skyler in the passenger seat, and Ryan and me in the back.

Because William had shared with me that he was especially into Ryan, it didn't make a whole lot of sense to me why William and Skyler were playing with each other's dicks on the drive to The Fruit. I mean, I didn't give a shit, but William had told me that Ryan was the guy that he was into…and I didn't get the sense that Ryan was especially keen on the front seat groping party that was going on, either. But whatever…

As per usual, The Fruit was hosting DJs who played a lot of techno music – meaning no lyrics, just beats. So it was a great thing that we'd loaded up all of the drugs we'd brought – as this music can be hard to really get into without the right mix of substances. But after so many crucial visits

165

to the bathroom, we all hit our stride and managed to feel the beat.

One of the dudes I was to be on the lookout for was David, a cute bisexual Jewish guy a couple of years younger than William. The other was a frat-tastic dude whose name I cannot remember. But that's okay – I think Mr. Fraternity figured out quickly that he'd been conned into buying a ticket to this event. He wasn't getting William's attention, so it wasn't long before he bounced. But damnit if David wasn't a confused puppy dog that evening... He was so sweet and so much happier that night before he realized William was there with Ryan.

William was a conundrum. I suppose he'd let David and the other guy believe they might go home with him after the show via social media. William had made it clear to Skyler and me that the post-show plans were to head back to my apartment for a sex party. Perhaps William figured these guys could be talked into participating, potentially? I cannot speak to the thoughts and feelings of other people. I was just there to have a good time. And I did. By that day in July, I knew where I stood with William. I'm not so sure that Ryan, Skyler, David, or Mr. Frat-boy had any clue where they fit into the mix.

David was 22 at the time, to William's 25. Ryan was 33. I was 32. (Ryan is one day shy of a year older than me, in fact, with his birthday being the day after mine.)

William seemed to be into Ryan, and Ryan into William as well. And yet, when this dude David tried to talk to William, William gave off the vibe that he was into David as well – even more so in the moments that Ryan wasn't by his side. I was introduced to David that evening, who was not oblivious to the mixed signals he was getting from William. David expressed that he'd pretty much come out that night because he thought he and William had a real connection based on whatever chatting they'd been doing prior to this event. But he felt a bit blown off in their interactions at the show. But David didn't let it totally ruin his night – it was just disappointing. I played the role of a supportive stranger as David explained his confusion over the situation. All I could say is that I'd ridden to the event with William, Skyler, and Ryan, but as to what anyone's motives or intentions were behind coming that evening, I had no idea. Get fucked up and have fun? That's why I was there – not to be anyone's therapist. And I managed to make that happen…It was a bit difficult to speak with David, as I couldn't make sense of why William had led this perfectly nice guy on, only to flaunt a relationship with Ryan in front of his face. But I could also tell Ryan wasn't oblivious to the presence of this David dude, who approached William a time or two with puppy dog eyes as if the two had planned to meet at the show and then hang for the night. (*Because they had…) There was no way to run interference on all of this – I didn't know what I was supposed to do to assuage the tension. I just kept bumping drugs and dancing the night away. After all, this was uncharted territory. I was just glad that the fratty dude who was also into William had already left. I just knew that this was a clusterfuck that only the **mastermind** knew the expectations for. And I was not the mastermind by any stretch.

The night wound down, and we went to leave. David was still a bit heartbroken and confused, but it seemed he'd be okay. Surely David could find someone in this bar to go home with, so long as he dried the well of tears from his eyes. David made a strong case to me as to why he was disappointed by how things went down. He felt deceived. And quite frankly, he was. William had gotten him to the event and then dropped the ball as though the dude had read the signals wrong. This wasn't what happened – William had set an expectation for the evening and then failed to deliver.

David and I ended up at an after-party at our mutual friend Katherine's apartment months later. This is where David made it clear that William had ghosted him, even though he hadn't done anything wrong. It was at this after-party that I got to hear David's side of things in detail. This is when I started to see that William had a tendency to discard people without giving much thought to the wreckage he left in his wake. Whether or not they deserved to be discarded was up for debate – I certainly should have been. But David didn't deserve this – I think I feel an extra level of empathy for David in this situation because he was so young. William said all of his boyfriends had been older, so Ryan was the obvious choice over David or the Frat Boy. And since William had given himself an unpaid position as The Fruit's promotions manager, I guess he felt he'd rather have the two guys buy tickets rather than lose the sale.

That night after The Fruit, we rode back to my apartment. Same seating arrangements in the car, with Ryan and I in the back seat. It wasn't until the radio started playing Sia's "Cheap Thrills" that I really got to see Ryan's personality shine… "Come on, come on, turn the radio on…" seemed to bring Ryan to life. All he communicated to me was something along the lines of, FINALLY-some-music-with-lyrics!!!!! And I was totally on the same page – there's only so much thump-thump music I could listen to in an evening before wondering where-the-fuck the lyrics were, also. Ryan had a big smile on his face as he sang, "no cheap thrills!" I was starting to see a glimpse of what William said he liked about this guy. As it turns out, he gives his heart and soul as a *restaurant manager*…although I will say, he sells himself short in some crucial ways.

The most authentic thing William ever brought to my attention was that Ryan is an awesome person. He is someone I am grateful to have in my life to this day. Because Ryan has always shared with me exactly how he feels and what he's thinking, from that **very first night** I met him.

Today, I know Ryan's backstory, and he's never polished it up or tried to edit it and present it in a way that is calculated to impress or paint some false narrative, which is a huge part of why I find him to be such an impressive person. There are so few people I meet in my personal life who let me see them for who they really are, in a genuine way.

Therapy clients let me see them fully because that's what they're in therapy to do – otherwise, what's the point? Ryan isn't guarded or deceptive, at least not with me. And I love him for his best parts and his worst parts. Because he tells me the worst parts. And to me, they're not so bad. I owe William a "thank you" for this introduction because five years later, William isn't in my life, but Ryan is. And that feels like a win-win. But now, back to the night we were introduced…

William had promoted the idea of having a four-way fuck-fest after The Fruit. But once we were back and settled, it became clear that not everyone was on the same page…

William and Skyler ended up on the (aforementioned) couch in my apartment, chatting it up. Meanwhile, I was in my kitchen with Ryan. And Ryan looked sad. He was speaking to me about how he still had feelings for his ex, Danny. He made it clear he liked William *alright,* but that ultimately, he hadn't healed from his last major break-up. Meanwhile, I could hear William -sitting on the same couch he'd sat on 6 or so months before, asking Skyler the same questions he'd posed the night I met him… "Tell me about your first time…" "What's your favorite sexual position?" "What's your number one fantasy?"…

WHAT THE FUCK? This was the first time I started questioning the authenticity of my friendship with William – if for no other reason than because his questions suddenly felt scripted. He'd originally stated, "I really wanna get to *know* you guys…" to me, Grant, and Enrique, and here he was, tossing out the same exact questions to Skyler – who had been a stranger to him when the night began. And Skyler appeared to be eating it up in much the same way that I had **the very first night.** It wasn't until I processed this revelation more completely that I began to wonder if these were the same questions he'd ask escorting clients to make them feel more comfortable. And while I've never posed this question to William directly, I did meet people before William rolled into town who subsequently met William and confirmed that William had been engaging in a way that made them feel like they were somehow special.

[**If you've ever heard the term "superficially charming," 3 people in this double book series embody that so perfectly. Can you figure out who they are?**]

But back to that night, when the expected sexual escapades were supposed to commence momentarily, back at my apartment. Skyler and I were in the living room with William, as Ryan had excused himself to the bedroom – which William had communicated was because he had a headache. I figured it had more to do with what he'd shared with me about his ex, Danny, although I didn't know Ryan well enough to have any actual read on whether or not this was impeding him from feeling sexual or whatever. What I did know was that my dick was out, hard, and that for a minute there, William was sitting on it. *This was different...*but it only lasted a split second before he decided he needed to go check on Ryan.

Not long after disappearing into my bedroom, William came out and announced that he and Ryan were leaving. William provided only limited information, but he essentially said Ryan was *uncomfortable.* Now, if I put myself in Ryan's shoes, I can only imagine why... Uncomfortable...??...with you clearly having multiple dudes lined up as your date for the evening? Or with you exchanging handy j's in the car with Skyler on the way to Durham? Or... had you not even bothered to tell Ryan that there was an orgy-expectation at the night's end? To this day, I have never asked Ryan directly *why* they left that evening when they did, but it's fair to say their relationship started from a place that was lacking in crucial aspects of communication.

CHAPTER 53

· · · · · · · ● · · · · · · ·

Okay, but...not fine at all....

Sometime in mid to late **August** 2018, Ryan and William broke up. When Ryan came over to my apartment the first time after they'd broken up, he was noticeably distraught. He was obviously sad over the breakup. There was clearly a lot on his mind, which was why he couldn't just **shake it off.** Ryan was trying to make sense of what had happened and why it had happened. He started relaying parts of their relationship to me. Troubling parts. Parts that I *thought* I had some insight into, but I didn't know what to do with the information...at least not immediately.

Ryan recalled being in bed with William. William went to the restroom. William's phone went off. He'd left it sitting by the bed – and Ryan saw a message from somebody wanting to meet up. Now that he'd seen the message, he couldn't unsee it. Ryan is not a confrontational person. And, of course, had the conversation about William escorting ever happened between them, there was room for an honest explanation. Or, if William insisted on keeping his secret, this text could have been explained away. No one can help it if a former FWB sends a message wanting to hook up, not knowing you're in a committed relationship. It's all about how you handle such a message at that moment...

When William returned to the room and glanced at his phone, he immediately announced he had to leave to go to Dunkin Donuts. It was an odd time of the day to be making a 'donut run', and Ryan knew - based on the way this was playing out - that William was clearly going to meet up for some kind of rendez-vous. Ryan knew, in that moment, that William was leaving to go meet up with some dude for sexual purposes and lying about it, as he put his clothes back on.

Ryan shared that it was moments like this that left him feeling unsettled about the relationship and about liking William in the first place. Ryan was left second-guessing the relationship: what was real and what wasn't. Ryan was sad they'd broken up - even though he knew William had lied about various things during their time together. They'd only dated a couple of months. Which was even more troublesome, given that's all the time it took for William to start having **illicit affairs**. And even if it had been a short-lived, **sad, beautiful, tragic love affair**, Ryan was really torn up over the whole thing.

Distance, timing, breakdown, fighting...Silence, the train runs off its tracks...
Kiss me, try to fix it, could you just try to listen?
Hang up, give up
and for the life of us we can't get back
    -**Sad Beautiful Tragic**, Taylor Swift

Seeing Ryan this sad was **treacherous.** I knew William had technically cheated on Ryan more than the times he knew about, but there was no room for *that* in this conversation.

I knew what had to be done – even if it did mean selling out a close friend of mine. I could no longer keep the secret that William had asked me to keep. I believed that if William left Ryan to go do sexual things with other dudes, it was likely based on a financial need - not because he intended to hurt Ryan. I had to believe that William was not *that* kind of person. For better or worse, I thought that sharing with Ryan that William was an escort would help relieve some of his heartache. William wasn't even speaking to Ryan at that time, anyway.

William had told me that he didn't intend to speak with Ryan any time soon – he was giving him space – and dead silence. Having heard both sides of the same break-up, I made the judgment call that Ryan didn't deserve this. So, I showed him William's Rentmen.com webpage, where he was soliciting men for sex. I let him know that *my guess* was that the text he'd intercepted was *probably* a client – not a romantic interest. I knew William cared about Ryan and that William knew Ryan was special, at least initially.

I can't say what this information meant to Ryan – after all, I'm not him. He already knew William had done porn, so this was less out-of-nowhere than it *could* have been. My hope was that it provided Ryan with some insight into why William had seemed so shady. It wasn't all in Ryan's head. And yet there was a financial motive for William's being shady. It wasn't personal. At least, I didn't think it was intended to be.

It's strange how your face
Doesn't look so innocent
Your secret has its consequence
and that's on you, babe...
     -Babe, Taylor Swift

I shared this information with Ryan sometime in late August or September of 2018. Ryan shared that suddenly it all made sense - the STI that William had been so insistent Ryan had brought into their relationship (...twice...) had surely just been William gaslighting the fuck out of him. Which Ryan said he sort of knew at the time, but having confirmation that William was an escort helped him to trust his gut feeling about the issue. But being a non-confrontational person, Ryan held this information in for much longer than I ever could have...

I hung out with Ryan and William individually during the time they were broken up. I didn't think they were going to reconcile, given that William was adamant they weren't.

Ryan seemed to be coming out of his sad phase in the weeks following the break-up.

Then, Ryan and I slept together. We were watching a movie and spooning, and it just kinda happened. And William had not lied – Ryan had (and still has, I'm sure…) a great dick.

Ryan and William reconnected in early October 2018.

Sometime in November, Ryan let me know he had PTO he had to burn. He was clear about one thing: He was headed out of the country for a vacation and didn't care who *was* or *was not* coming with him. He was going – no one was holding him back…

Ryan was adamant about this point because he and I were both used to William sharing info about upcoming trips he was scheduled to take, only to have them fall through repeatedly for unknown reasons. Plans were canceled, or William missed his flight – who knows? Ryan was booking a trip to Mexico, and I was invited if I wanted to go. William could come if he wanted to or stay home if he couldn't. The same went for me. Ryan was going with or without us. I booked my plane ticket and strongly encouraged William to figure out how the fuck he was going to make it work. And he made it work.

CHAPTER 54

• • • • • • **•** • • • • • •

Mexico

In December of 2018, the three of us went down to Playa Del Carmen, Mexico.

Ryan never shared with William that he knew William was a sex worker. And Ryan and William were back together.

I was going with them as the identifiable third wheel of the trip – with the explicitly stated promise that they would not leave me *feeling* like a third wheel. (**Note: that did not mean we were going to have a ménage-à-trois situation. After all, they had their own bedroom downstairs, and I had mine upstairs. It just meant that they wouldn't be doing couples activities the whole time. And, true to their word, they did not). It also meant that if I needed to get laid, they weren't going to be cock blocking. (**I *needed to ensure none of us would be leaving Mexico with blue balls – especially me!*).

I felt like we did a good job of balancing the time spent, all three of us, and the time we went our separate ways. We wandered the town together, exploring, that first day or two. At some point, I came across a casino and got stuck there for a couple of days…but how could I not? Given the exchange rate, gambling with pesos felt like gambling with Monopoly money. During my days gambling, William and Ryan knew exactly where to find me, and they would drop by and check in from time to time.

Our accommodations were awesome! We had a two-story condo with a jacuzzi on the upper level – where my room was located. And rooftop access, so there was a great view of the skyline and of the downtown area. We weren't far from the beach, either, which we took advantage of. All three of us went beach walking one of the first days of the trip, and then I think William and Ryan went back a time or two when I was in the casino. We went out to eat as a trio a few times as well. I let them know any time they needed privacy, I could get out of their hair. After all, the Airbnb where we were staying allowed us to walk just about anywhere we could possibly want to go. So, if they needed me to step out so they could fuck around, I was happy to give them the space. But this was not a request they ever made.

William's behavior was highly suspect/confusing, and instilled paranoia in Ryan that was completely unnecessary. I understand that partners sometimes need space from one another, but William would ask for it in the strangest ways. William would either tell Ryan *that he* was going out while insisting Ryan stay at the Airbnb until he got back or letting Ryan know they needed to split up and walk in opposite directions through the city. William said they could reconvene to spend time together later but that he didn't want to see him again until at least *x-amount* of time had passed (often times, an hour). And then he would disappear.

Ryan was left speculating about who William was going to hook up with. Other times, William insisted he was going to score drugs of some kind (which made little sense, as we had plenty…). Sometimes, we would reunite, and all was well. But not every time…

The unfortunate thing about this trip, which was a lot of fun overall, was that much of whether we were having a good time depended on William's mood. I'd never known William's mood to be this erratic. But he seemed to have no problem inflicting how he was feeling on me or, more frequently, on Ryan.

One of the times William returned from one of his solo missions, Ryan and I were up in my room listening to and talking about Eminem. Ryan and I are both big fans, and that is something we bonded over early on in our friendship. William listened to the conversation long enough to be mad about it. It pissed William off that during the time he'd gone off on his own, Ryan and I had laughed *without him*. That resulted in more of an argument between the two of them, so I can't say much about how it went. I can just comment that it was things like this that made the trip that should have been completely lovely a bit more stressful than it needed to be. Ryan later shared that William had been mad because it seemed that me and Ryan had more in common than the two of them did.

William frustrated me directly (and seemingly intentionally) when I'd asked both of them if I could have the place to myself to hook up with a dude that I wanted to have over. They were both cool with that, just like they'd said they would be before we'd even left the US. The place we were staying was very open, and since my room was essentially loft-style, it lacked any sound barriers to the downstairs. Despite initially being agreeable, William had a change of heart – right before my guest arrived. He literally crossed his arms in front of his chest and laid face-down in his bed, refusing to move or even speak to whatever was going through his mind. I got irritated enough to raise my voice, which I rarely do, but it seemed he was just trying to be difficult for the sake of being difficult. I still don't know what was going through his head at the time or why he was behaving like a toddler whenever the mood struck him. But Ryan and I are chill people, so aside from William's attempt to cock block me, I kept my cool. And he finally got up and went outside the condo long enough for me to hook up with this Mexican-tennis-player-bottom. He was a fun time.

Something inspirational that happened while in Mexico was that there was a painting I liked hanging in my bedroom at our Airbnb. I took a photo of it because I wanted to try to recreate it once we were back in the US. And once I did, I kept painting my own stuff from there and never looked back. I now have an apartment full of paintings! I've even sold a few (although I'm much more likely to just give them away any time someone says they like a particular one). The Mexico trip inspired me to dive headfirst into this hobby, which I enjoy immensely.

We had a blast that December in Playa Del Carmen, and it was sad to have to go. But we had to get back to The States. And so up...up...and awaaaayyyyy we went.

CHAPTER 55

· · · · · · · ● · ● · · · · ·

So Casually Cruel, In the Name of Being Honest

At some point, I knew it was bound to come out. After all of William's shadiness in Mexico – trying to get away from Ryan and then disappearing for chunks of time…It was shocking to me how long Ryan was able to keep William's secret to himself. I cannot imagine how Ryan was able to go back to dating William and not address the pink elephant in the room, but he did. For a little while, anyway…

In late January 2019, the cat was out of the bag. William called me, and he was pissed. He wanted to know why the fuck I had told Ryan about his side hustle. And so I told William the truth – that I'd told Ryan during the period of time when the two were broken up because Ryan had told me about William leaving for 'Dunkin Donuts' after getting a text message from a guy who randomly wanted to hang out, and that seeing Ryan so sad when William wouldn't speak to him – it just seemed to make sense to tell him, given that otherwise William just looked like a cheater. At least…that was going to be my speech…I can't remember how much he let me get through before he lost interest or cut me off. It was not a long phone call. I think he understood that I had a *reason* for telling Ryan, and it wasn't just to make William look bad. But he was still angry with me.

Keeping this type of secret from someone who had become a pretty good friend just felt like a dick thing to do. And it seemed like something William would have at least attempted to tell Ryan *at some point* if he was serious about the relationship. OR he would have stopped escorting and taken down his Rentmen ad, at least.

I don't have any regrets about telling Ryan. I'd certainly want someone to tell me.

CHAPTER 56

· · · · · · · ● · · · · · · · ·

The End of an Era...

Well...that's a bit dramatic of a chapter title...I'm going to try and keep this part short and sweet because most of this is not my story to tell...

According to Ryan, he and William broke up on St. Patrick's Day 2019.

I was surprised they'd made it that long, given the difficulties I witnessed in Mexico. William forgave me for telling Ryan he was an escort. And hey, if I had done it *just* to be an asshole, I would get it if he hadn't ever forgiven me. But Ryan wears his heart on his sleeve, and I can't stand to see his eyes looking sad. So I told him. And William got over it.

There was at least one time before they broke up that I went over to the house where William was living to hang out with William when Ryan was working. William inquired, "Hey Bruce...have you seen or talked to Ryan lately?" I hadn't seen him since we'd gotten back from Mexico, in fact. Which is exactly what I told William. William responded, letting me know, "Ryan is not the person *we* thought he was...He has *changed*..." I never knew what William meant by this statement. I knew William had changed since I met him, but to me, Ryan seemed to be the same, genuine Ryan I'd always thought he was. Although what I said to William *was* true...I hadn't seen Ryan since we'd returned from Mexico – and that had been a couple of months ago at the time of this conversation.

CHAPTER 57

• • • • • • • ● • • • • • •

Back to December, 2018.
(Perspective taking)

**Knowing what I know NOW, present day, late 2023, I have a whole new perspective on this entire exchange. This lightbulb JUST lit up as I was typing this...

At the time, William inquired, "Have you seen Ryan lately?" I figured he'd wanted to get my answer before he told me that "Ryan has *changed*" because he knew that if I *had* seen him, I would know this wasn't true...But *today*, I know that Ryan had started sleeping with his ex, Danny, towards the end of his relationship with William. My guess is that if William was ever suspicious about where Ryan was going or where he had been, Ryan may very well have told William he'd been hanging out with **Me!** After all, I'd gone to Mexico with the two of them – so Ryan could drop *my* name because I wasn't a threat. So...*if* I'm *right*...then in this moment when I let William know that I <u>had not</u> seen or heard from Ryan since we'd returned from Mexico a couple of months prior, it may've hit William at that moment that Ryan had been lying to him. That would totally make sense. Why else would William determine – at that moment – that Ryan was not the person *we* thought he was? (I thought William was operating like a **mastermind,** but I'm now questioning this original assumption, all these years later...) I always thought William's comment was an odd comment to make, but if the scenario I'm spelling out has any truth to it, it makes complete sense. Because if Ryan told William he'd hung out with me and he'd been MIA for any length of time, William would have realized at that moment that Ryan lied about where he was and who he was with. The logical conclusion for why Ryan would feel the need to lie was that he was fucking someone else – most likely his ex! **Checkmate, I couldn't lose.** Perhaps Ryan forgot to clue me into the lie...or, more likely, there was no reason to tell me because he dropped the lie when William was mad at me, so William and I weren't speaking, anyway. I'm realizing now that I probably inadvertently blew Ryan's cover when I to William we had not seen each other. Whoops...(although truthfully, I am glad I wasn't asked to lie. William had already put me in that position over his gigolo-job, I did not need Ryan asking me to lie on his behalf if and when he was spending time with his ex...).

    Question...?: **Ryan started cheating on William with his ex, who he still had feelings for. So...does that make him the bad guy?...hmmm...

    Now if I flip script and look at things through Ryan's eyes and attempt to see things and speak from his perspective...*of course* I'm going to fuck my ex, Danny, who I was *in love* with! I learned that my *new* boyfriend, William - who broke my heart and who I'm now back together with – has been an *escort* behind my back the entire time we've been dating! – and never told me! In fact, I'd feel like I had the golden ticket to fuck whoever the hell I wanted to! Because having a boyfriend never stopped William from slinging his dick, so I (Ryan) now had every reason to cheat on him if I felt like it, right?...hell, he's probably still banging dudes behind my back, anyway... Plus, I've been in love with Danny this whole time...for better or worse, William has helped me remember how much I love someone else...

    **William was a secret gigolo. He asked Bruce to keep this secret from Ryan, and he never told Ryan about all of the dudes he was banging for money during their relationship. So, does that mean William is the bad guy in this story..??..

Through the reader's eyes Wait, hold up: Wasn't Bruce originally *William*'s friend? And yet, he threw William under the bus about being an escort - to Ryan - when Ryan and William were broken up...(*some friend*!?!..does loyalty mean anything to this dude?) Also, didn't he mention that he and Ryan fucked when Ryan and William were broken up? And all the while he was maintaining a friendship with William? (...seriously!?!?...) Finally, didn't he travel to Mexico with these two dudes, keeping the secret that he told Ryan about the escorting, AND keeping the secret from William that he'd hooked up with Ryan while the two were broken up?

**This Bruce dude – HE sounds like the real bad guy!!

My point is: no matter who the reader feels is the worst of the villains, it's fair to say none of us were our *best* selves during this period. William didn't inspire me to be a **Better Man**, but I didn't inspire him to be one, either. We did have some fun times together, but from the very start, it was bound to be a problematic relationship. I never judged him for being in porn or for escorting – plus I appreciated that he was honest about it (with me) from the start. If I'd been in a better headspace when he initially told me he really liked this dude named Ryan but that he was keeping the escorting stuff a secret, I would have challenged him: Don't you think if you *really* like him, you should be *honest* with him?...OR, *at the very least,* STOP escorting immediately!? But that is not what I did. Not only did I not challenge William to do something different, I also co-signed the bullshit by agreeing to keep my mouth shut about William's (non-photography-based) profession. *My excuse...and I'm aware that it IS an excuse...is that if I had encouraged William to be honest about this, I wouldn't be certain I wasn't at least partially hoping Ryan would break things off with William over it. Because while my feelings for William weren't as intense as they had once been, they still existed. I was reminded of this when William first mentioned that there was this really cool guy he'd met named Ryan, and he wanted me to meet him and* *give my honest opinion. This request was both a compliment and a swift-kick-to-the-balls, all in one. So, yeah. While today's me knows I had an opportunity to encourage William to do the right thing – to be a* **Better Man** *– in that moment, it wasn't clear to me if I could encourage him to be honest with absolute certainty that I didn't have ulterior motives…*

But whatever the truth is, thinking about things from all perspectives has helped me to realize…

NO ONE I'VE WRITTEN ABOUT IS ALL BAD. NO ONE I'VE WRITTEN ABOUT – (myself, especially) – IS ALL GOOD. I am a person-centered therapist who truly believes we're all just doing the best we can, and we ALL strive to be *better.* But perhaps everyone's definition of what "better" means is different. One person may believe that being unconditionally kind to your fellow man is what "better" looks like. Another person may decide that amassing a boatload of cash is what "better" looks like and that having the cutest young boyfriend is also a marker that you are "better." The value placed on hard work or cunning may be "better" to one person, while values like charity or love may be a top priority to someone else. Who's to say which values shine brighter? When I started writing, I was under the impression that I was the ultimate authority on what values made someone a *better man* and could, therefore, judge who was falling short. But I'm starting to see it's a bit more complicated than that.

I hope reading these words will encourage people to examine their impact on others and the world around them. And if they aren't totally comfortable with where they land, maybe they'll do something different…

CHAPTER 58

· · · · · · · · ● · · · · · · ·

Healing from Trauma

Healing from traumatic experiences typically involves pulling something positive from what was an overall negative experience. It's not an easy feat to achieve, mentally, without outside help. Finding something about a traumatic experience that is worth holding onto, worth remembering…be it something about yourself that you learned or some meaning behind why the trauma happened to you in the first place – can be tricky. Working through trauma intentionally with a mental health professional typically leaves the person more aware of their own resilience. It can become more apparent to someone how much strength they possess and how brave they truly are for facing a trauma head-on rather than avoiding it. And it can leave the person with important life lessons about other people and about how to navigate the world moving forward.

When I do an intake with a new therapy client, I ask the person, "have you ever been through anything traumatic?" This question is intentionally vague, both because I want it left up to client interpretation while also recognizing that when someone is first meeting with me, they may not feel ready to disclose their entire trauma history. The client will often respond with, "Well…what counts as 'trauma'?" or, "What do *you* consider to be 'traumatic'?" I respond by saying, "It doesn't matter what *I* think. What matters is your experience. If *you* found something to be traumatic, whatever it was, that's what counts…" People will then explain their history of being bullied in middle school or feeling neglected while growing up in their big family, and others will comment on past romantic partners who mistreated them in any number of ways.

Some therapists make the distinction between "Big T" Traumas and "little t" traumas, with the "Big T's" being events that were life-threatening or that involved bodily violation or harm. These aren't terms I typically use, but for this point, I would say that I have had some "little t" traumatic relationships that, until now, I hadn't ever unpacked. I've surprised myself with how much I had to say and how much emotion I still hold onto. I recognize that it's not really any of what happened in the relationships that continue to plague my mind. In fact, I don't think about my past relationships on a conscious level much, if at all. What bothers me is the fact that it is my past experiences that shape my behavior and my thinking today, and it is these 'little t traumas' that are ultimately holding me back. Something significant, meaningful, or positive has got to come from my collective experiences with dating as a gay man in this lifetime. That may not be me finding my **superstar** to settle down with, but it could mean someone benefitting from reading what I wrote or learning something from my experience so they don't have to go through it themselves.

*Suggested listen? **Superstar** -Taylor Swift

For years now, whenever someone has asked me, "So, is there anyone special?...", I have an extremely relationship-averse reaction. I'll play it off with half-truths or with a joke. After all, who wants to hear I'm a therapist who hasn't worked through his own relationship trauma? So instead, I'll say, "Being in a relationship would get in the way of my sex life..." or "I see enough dysfunctional couples in therapy to know it's just not for me..." But those reasons hardly scratch the surface of why I don't pursue a relationship. The real reasons why I don't pursue anyone include:

1)   I do not trust myself to pick a partner.
2)   I don't want to be responsible for someone else becoming addicted to drugs. Especially not someone I care about! (*It can really alter the course of someone's life! I always knew*

I wanted to be a therapist. I worked hard to become one! But a meth addicted therapist? That was never my intent.)

The things that shape my outlook and attitudes towards putting myself out there and dating again all seem to tie back to past relationships, unhealed trauma, and my morals and values.

13 years after my relationship with Jon first began, there have been about 30 days total where I have not used meth. I work way too much and have not found the time to take a break long enough to get off the drug. Is that an excuse? Absolutely. But I can't simply disappear for an indefinite length of time so that I can detox. None of my clients or colleagues know that I've been drug-addicted the entire time I've been a therapist.

They say we're only as sick as our secrets...I guess this means I'm pretty sick.

And it doesn't feel good.

CHAPTER 59

•••••• • •••••••

Jump then Fall

For anyone who is not addicted to crystal meth and who has not been using it daily for over a decade, that is awesome - I would not wish an addiction on anyone. But to clue you in on what it is like to be addicted to this drug from day-to-day, I'll paint you a picture.

In the early days of meth use, I didn't need nearly as much sleep, I didn't eat much, I had an overwhelming appetite for sex, and I always had the energy to do…well…everything. I was also in my early 20s, and so it was a time when everyone was thinner than they are now (in terms of my peers). Genetically, I was predestined to sweat more than most people, and living in the humid southeast and being an active person also contributed. But meth is the reason I've sweated my ass off in many-a-night-club, circuit parties, and raves. The meth-and-Percocet combo Jon used to give me made me the biggest sweaty mess, but meth on its own does a pretty solid job, too.

Jon always stuck to a rule when it came to using meth, and that was to sleep. So even though we would have marathon sex until four or five AM, afterwards, sleep was next on the agenda. So, while many people may be spun up for days to the point of seeing 'shadow people', that is not my story.

Eventually, the appetite-suppressing effects of meth also cease to exist. Any time I've been around 'meth people' and I suggest we order a pizza, everyone looks at me like, "What the fuck did you just say?" Food used to be the furthest thing from my mind when using meth, but the 'meth people' I'm referring to are not people who have used it daily for as long as I have. (That is NOT a brag. Trust me.) Because no one I've met – aside from Jon – has used meth as consistently as I have for as long as I have. When I say it was our morning cup of coffee, I am not kidding. And that's how it has been for as long as I can remember at this point. I don't smoke a bowl and suddenly start acting differently. I don't frantically clean my apartment the way I once would. I don't stop eating or sleeping altogether. And I don't start picking my face or getting paranoid. Meth, for me, has become a useful morning pick-me-up and a way to greet the day. And I am well aware that this is not normal.

Anyone prescribed stimulant ADHD medication *may* be able to relate to a degree – after all, they're both amphetamines. And anyone who takes stimulants every day at the same dose for long enough has probably also had the experience of the medication becoming less effective over time (*again, that's with daily use – if you take breaks over weekends or holidays, this may not be your experience with stimulant medication). It is for these reasons that I have been able to use meth for as long as I have without raising any alarm bells. I can certainly become animated or get overly excited, but not in the way that someone relatively new to meth use does.

So why do I still use it?

Well, that's another problematic part. If I were to stop using meth cold turkey, I would go into hibernation. And after this many years of using, I am imagining that what was once a three-day recovery period may now be something that resembles an actual depressive episode (which, as a therapist, I know means it must be a stretch of at least two weeks to meet diagnostic criteria as such). And while I've given a lot of thought to faking a 'vacation' and getting the inevitable hibernation underway, as I may have mentioned before, I am a terrible liar. Having colleagues ask me, "Oh, how was your vacation?" or "Where'd you end up going?" would likely result in a lot of stuttering, sweating, and incoherent answers to seemingly benign questions. When I say I am NOT good at lying, what I mean is I don't get away with it – my behavior gives me away. Not to mention, I'm scared to be meth free. I'm scared of what's on **the other side of the door.**

I will say that the idea of continuing to know my health is deteriorating because of this drug is creating an ever-increasing amount of anxiety within me as well. When the pain gets great enough, people change. Bodily (lung) pains coupled with anxiety around how much I've shortened my own life span by using this drug are catching up to me. I have been in the pre-contemplation stage of change for quite some time now. Before I actually lose teeth to this drug, I really need to do something different.

So today (September 15th, 2023), I'm checking myself into detox.

Don't blame me, your love made me crazy, if it doesn't you aint doin' it right...

I finally realized I didn't want to be ...**using for the rest of my life.** -Taylor Swift, **Don't Blame Me**

The following are my journal entries from two days in detox...

CHAPTER 60

• • • • • • • ● • • • • • •

Day 1

So, on day one, I got checked in. I had dinner (the food here is delicious!...and I'm not being sarcastic). I went to an AA meeting. I headed back to my room, and as I was flipping through the channels, the first music channel I landed on was the tail end of the **Anti-hero** music video. I'm going to take that as encouragement to keep writing while I'm here. (Something about big Taylor meeting up with the two rooftop Taylors makes me feel both encouraged and inspired to keep sharing...)

It has been so long since I've gone any amount of time without (what the gays call) Tina (...or what straight people in Atlanta call "tweak"...). So I'm sitting here wondering, "How hard is this crash going to be?" I'm anticipating I'll be comatose in a couple of days...

My phone was dying at intake. I had enough battery to inform my little brother that I'd be missing in action for a week, so if anyone was looking for me, they'd be SOL...He wrote back, "Have fun on your gaycation!" – LMFAO. I've got a friend as well as a backup person checking in on my dogs, but the friend is recovering from hernia surgery, and so when I went to drop off the keys, I had to be quick about it, as his boyfriend (who hates me) could return at any minute. (He has every right to hate me – I'm in love with his boyfriend). So...that friend knows I'm in detox, my brother knows I'm MIA, and I told my kickball team captain because I'd be missing multiple practices before our first game on Sunday (which I should be out in time for)...then back to work on Monday.

CLOSURE

I will note – day one of detox, I realized it feels weird to socialize with people here because meth really has had an impact on my comfort level in just having casual conversations with new people. While simultaneously, since no one here knows what I do for work, there's a level of increased comfort. I hope no one asks me what I do because I'm a terrible liar, and I don't want to lie, but I also don't want to talk about it. I'm low-key paranoid that a client of mine could show up any moment and check themselves in…I have no idea how I'd react to that situation (grab a clipboard and fake like I'm staff? I don't fucking know…?)

I was just speaking to my roommate outside about past mistakes made when using substances, and I felt oddly comfortable not having to censor myself. But I feel like if my profession comes to light with my fellow inpatients, I won't be able to speak about my substance abuse problem anymore out of fear.

CHAPTER 61

•••••••• • •••••••

Day 2

As predicted, I'm dead-to-the-world tired. I made it to breakfast, returned to my room, and passed out. I had a dream that one of my male therapy clients and Taylor Swift came over to my apartment and were discussing a Farside comic where dogs were Nazis and the entire human race were the Jews. *It was very weird.* When the mental health technician came in to see if I felt like going to yoga, which I initially said I'd attend, I declined. I was hoping to get back to my **wildest dreams,** but Taylor was a no-show. The doctor came in to do my physical and asked me many of the same questions as the intake person yesterday afternoon, and the nurse did during my assessment last night. He seemed caught off guard when I said my profession...

He also said I just needed rest when I inquired about Wellbutrin, as I'd read it could be helpful with meth withdrawal. Despite feeling incredibly tired, I was able to get in the shower after the doctor left. He was very nice and seemed to care a lot more than the doc I worked with most recently at a different mental health hospital in the area. Speaking of, even with their masks on, I recognized a couple of the nurses from my time working as the weekend therapist at the other facility I'm referring to. It's both uncomfortable and familiar to be in my shoes in this moment, being on the other side of things. I'm yet to meet with a therapist, but they tend to be more scarce on weekends at mental health facilities anyway. Lunch is soon...

After lunch, I returned to my room and turned on Netflix. Side note: this detox facility is far nicer than any I've ever worked in. My roommate and I each have our own tv! Anyway, I wouldn't typically turn on a movie called "Love at First Sight", but the girl…excuse me…the young woman from White Lotus, season two, is in it and that show is too funny so I couldn't resist. I had my blood drawn earlier, but I'm going to go ahead and call it before seeing the results – my testosterone must be low because tears were a-flowin' waaay prematurely…and while I'm not typically a rom-com person, this movie gave me some hope. Maybe on the other side of detox…when I don't have an addiction to inflict on a partner…maybe, just maybe, I'll find my **Romeo**…the **King of my Heart.** But maybe I won't. And maybe I'll move forward, meth free…and maybe I won't. But if I do use it again, it won't be anyone's fault but my own.

It's carrying around the resentment that's been the worst part. And every day, there's been a barrier between me and meeting someone amazing… every day wondering if my gums are receding or pondering what my skin would look like if I hadn't been using for the past 13 years…all of that resentment can finally dissipate. The optimism I once had about finding someone awesome can be restored. (Maybe?....)

Sometimes, life choices, circumstances, and people can derail your trajectory. But at some point, you have to reclaim personal responsibility. I'm embarrassed by how long it took me to really own this. But it's better to figure it out at 37 than never.

*****Flashback Over*********

CHAPTER 62

·····•·•·•·•·•·•·····

What A Dick

A couple of weekends ago, I was out at a bar, and a dude kissed me. He found me as he was getting ready to walk out the back door of the nightclub my team had gone to after our game. He let me know that this was it: our last chance to kiss. Take it or leave it.

He'd been flirting with me when we were at the last bar and on the walk over to this bar. He'd always been nice to me, enthusiastic, and fun to be around. And I think he's cute. Very cute, in fact. But I never thought anything of it or that anything between us could happen beyond friendship. After all, he's engaged.

So when he commented that I better quit – I was getting him hard - as we were walking from one bar to the next, I was caught off guard, to say the least (I wasn't doing anything especially sexual, just being myself). And while we never hooked up, I can confirm that I got that kiss before he left that night. And he's a good kisser.

But that asshole went and woke up these goddam butterflies. The last thing I want is to be crushing on a dude who can never be **mine**. He's kind, athletic, and charming. And I want to punch him in his perfect teeth. **All I feel in my stomach is butterflies...** meanwhile, he's **got a** guy **at home and everybody knows that, everybody knows that...**

We kissed at the club, with his significant other less than 100 yards away. In my defense, I didn't know if his relationship was open or closed at the time. But I now know it was officially not okay for him to be kissing me....

196

It would be a fine proposition if I was a stupid girl...

And yeah I might go with it, if I hadn't once been just like her...

Girl at home, -Taylor Swift

To break down that lyric and apply it here...Unlike Taylor, I'd "go with it" – he's **Gorgeous** – and maybe that makes me a 'stupid girl.' But if he weren't spoken for, I just might try and marry him.

[I wonder if I'm more attracted to him *because* he's taken..? As I mentioned, somehow, I find myself attracted to toxic guys and toxic situations...is that why I think he's cute? That would make sense...]

But maybe, just maybe, I am learning lessons and 'detoxifying', if you will...kicking 'toxic' to the curb - in many different ways...I told this man he is still one of my league favorites. And he is. Now I've just gotta figure out how to kill the butterflies. No more sexy messages were sent. And *that's* called progress, not perfection, baby. Because a mistake is only a mistake if you don't learn anything from it. This dude taught me that kissing single people when you're engaged is a dick move. Because <u>you</u> went home to <u>him</u>, and I went home *thinking* about <u>you</u>.

If I'm ever engaged, I fully intend on remembering this valuable life lesson.

Don't let those **loose lips sink ships** on a Sunday night. (Or **all the damn time.**)

What a dick? Maybe....but sadly, I'll never know...

Lol.

*Suggested listen: **Say Don't Go**, -Taylor Swift (**Taylor's Version of 1989 dropped yesterday, after I'd already written this chapter. I do not know how she does it, but she officially has a song that fits just about every romantic encounter I've ever had...)

So that's pretty much where I am today. I'm grateful for that dick from the last chapter because he reminded me that the butterflies can still come back to life. I haven't allowed myself the possibility of butterflies in such a long time, but this guy managed to get them stirring when my guards were down. This came at an opportune time, as I have found writing over the past couple of months to be a long-overdue opportunity for healing. I still have a hate/love relationship with those butterflies, but knowing they can still kick into high gear gives me a lot of hope. I'd still **like to be my old self again**, and **I'm still trying to find it...** - still looking for that ever-optimistic hopeless romantic person I once was. Having gotten all this out of my system and down on paper, I feel more connected to my old self than I have in a very long time. I feel a renewed optimism that my romantic life is not **dead and gone and buried** after all. And THAT is a shift that will make living my life day-to-day A LOT better. And so, **dear reader**, thank you for coming with me on this journey.

And THANK YOU, again, to **Taylor Swift** - for all your support along the way. For all of the fans you've met who haven't been able to speak during meet-and-greet opportunities because they were sobbing uncontrollably, here's the second in a two-book series that illustrates why. Your lyrics weave their way into the lives of your fans and allow us to feel like someone gets it. Gets US. Whether we're hurting or blissfully in love. Wait, wait, wait...this needs to be its own section...

Dear Taylor...

....

..Oh, jeez...*now* I'm at a loss for words...

The idea that you (Taylor Swift) may *actually* read ...this one day is somehow making it more difficult to write...

CLOSURE

Well, perhaps that's my jumping-off point...

Dear Taylor,

Attempting to put into words how much your music has meant to me is simply something I cannot begin to do. It would be impossible to capture that with words...correction: it would be impossible *for **Me!*** to capture that with words. YOU could do it beautifully, I'm certain. But that would sort of defeat the purpose...lol. So instead, I'm going to tell a few random stories in an attempt to paint a picture of what you and your music mean to me. Forgive me for being presumptuous – I'll be writing as if you've read <u>Better Man</u> and <u>Closure</u>, which I realize you may not have. And you may never read this. But I'm going to type it out as if you have all the time in the world...since you're never busy or anything... ☺

I'd estimate it was sometime in 2007 when I texted my younger sister, Lee Anne, letting her know: "Taylor Swift should be your role model." Her response was simply, "Bruce, I'm older than her." I mean, fair enough, since role models are typically people we 'look up to', and all. In retrospect, I see my sister's point...but at the time, I'm pretty sure I did the obnoxious older brother thing and tried to convince her why she should take this suggestion into consideration. *Plus*, it's only the difference of June vs. December **1989**, we're talking about...

In the chapter "Dear Reader," I make mention of a trip I took out to California (where I tried to get Jon to drop my car off for repairs...but that part is irrelevant...). Basically, my aunt had planned a trip where all of my adult cousins and I flew out to California to visit my Uncle John, his wife, and their two kids. At some point on the trip, someone was flipping through a People magazine, and my cousin Will made a comment about how Jennifer Aniston and Taylor Swift, two beautiful, successful women, seemed to have so much trouble finding love and stable relationships.

My aunt – who, in her defense, is truly a lovely person, scrunched her face and commented to my cousin that he should *not* put *those two* women in the same category! After all, Jennifer Aniston is American's sweetheart, and **who's Taylor Swift anyway? Ew...** - not her exact words, but certainly the sentiment on this day in June of 2009. I don't think I spoke to my aunt for the rest of the trip. Intentionally.

The backstory here is that I had lived with my aunt towards the end of high school (so, 2004...) because I wasn't getting along with my divorced parents. During the time I lived with her, I burned her a CD with songs that were especially significant and sentimental in our relationship. At some point in 2009, my aunt commented that she wished I would make her another CD because she'd appreciated the thought I put into the first one so much. Well, at least half of the songs I'd thought to put on version 2.0 were your songs!! So when my aunt eye-rolled and commented that she just didn't get what all the fuss over Taylor Swift was about, the kindest thing I could do in the face of such ignorance was walk away. I have never been as disappointed in my aunt as I was at this moment. Literally. Because aside from this blunder, my aunt is a wonderful person. And she had no idea that I took her judgmental and flippant comment as a personal attack. I don't typically care about someone's opinions related to celebrity gossip – it's not a topic of conversation I get wrapped up in. But when it was *you*, I saw **Red.** This is the only time I can think of where someone got a 'pass' – after all, she had paid to fly us all out to Cali, put us up in hotel rooms, and paid for tickets to various adventures. I've been known to get up-in-arms when people say rude things about you, Taylor. But this time, I had **it in myself to go with grace...**

But wait! This story is not the spirit of what I'm trying to convey...I'm going to leave it in, but what I want to focus more on is how much your music has done to unite people, not divide them! For example...

CLOSURE

My kickball team! Taylor, I am part of an amazing kickball team called Big Kick Energy. We are part of Stonewall Sports, an LGBT+ league here in Raleigh. I love my team. And a lot of them love you! As an aside, I typed out a hilarious group chat exchange from early September 2023, when I started writing <u>Better Man</u>, that will illustrate how you came to be so intricately woven into the fabric of my story – as I was creating it – so much so that trying to extract you from it was an impossibility. Not that I would have wanted to! But I'd pretty much written the entire first book before it dawned on me that copyright issues were a thing…but anyway…

I took your lyric **"make the friendship bracelets, take the moment and taste it"**, and put it into practice. Everyone on my team has a personalized friendship bracelet (because I bought way too many beads in anticipation of the **Eras Movie** premiere…), and the bracelets are really funny. We lost our first couple of games, but the day everyone got their bracelets, we won for the first time. And last weekend, we won both games in our double-header. So, since we got our bracelets, we've been undefeated, lol. So, thank you for that.

Update: added January 23rd, 2024: Big Kick Energy won the division championship. We never lost another game after the friendship bracelets were handed out, which included winning back-to-back-to-back-to-back games (that's 4 in 1 day!) to seal the 2023 Fall Kickball Championship victory. Yay BKE!!!

Taylor, I don't know how long you've been following me, but it must have been for a very long time. Because **"I'm only me when I'm with you"** was clearly written about *my* best friendship with Britt. (*to any nosey people reading my personal letter to Taylor, no, I'm not crazy…I know Taylor is too busy to *still* stalk me…I'm just suggesting she did it back when Britt and I became best friends decades ago…duh…Now, butt-out, this is just for Taylor…) Britt and I have been best friends for more than 20 years now. And she is the reason I bought beads galore because without

Britt, I wouldn't know that showing up to the premiere of The Eras Tour Movie without friendship bracelets would

leave me feeling less connected. And as a shameless-gay-white-man-who-bought-a-last-minute-ticket-to-your-1989-Tour-concert-in-Raleigh-and-danced-harder-than-any-teenage-girl-in-the-arena, I know what it's like to be **on the outside**...but thanks to Britt, at this event, that was never going to happen...

    **if anyone is closely scrutinizing this picture, Britt and I are well aware that "Fuck John Mayer" is not a Taylor Swift song...any more than "TAY TAY TAY" is...and that "Gaylor" is not her name...But YOU aren't even supposed to be reading this part, anyway...so...

    ...back to my new friend...

Taylor,

    At the risk of shifting the mood, my step-mom lost her daughter MK when MK had a heart transplant that her body rejected. She was eleven years old. She was my sister, Lee Anne's best friend. And *my* best friend, Britt...that is MK's sister. (*the same Britt who helped me to make all of these bracelets, who flew in from St. Simon's to see the Era's Tour movie with me AND who told me about the friendship bracelets we absolutely had to make before the premiere.) So, where am I going with this? When **Red (Taylor's Version)** was released, my stepmom remarked that she'd been jamming out to it non-stop. We started chit-chatting about how great it was with all of the new music. My stepmom mentioned having a favorite song from the album. She couldn't remember the name of it, so I just kept blurting out track after track off the top of my head. My stepmom kept saying, "No, not that one…" **Ronan** was the answer to the riddle. Of course. My point? Your music **hits differently** for different people, depending on their personal experiences. But anyone with an open mind can become a Swiftie. If they aren't already, they probably just haven't had a personal playlist that was (wait for it…) Ta(i)ylor-made. Love you, Taylor!

Part of illustrating how important you are in my life was going to include a story about the last time I saw Nathan, my most terrible ex. He really pissed me off because he used you to get under my skin. I was going to talk about how this led to me kicking him out of my apartment and finally setting a boundary with him to not contact me, which he has respected now for almost a year, but **Mr. Perfectly Fine** just started playing on my phone, and it reminded me to bypass the details of that story and highlight what matters: He now has every song from every album of yours on his phone. It doesn't matter to me if it's because he's a bit obsessive…or if it's because he finally realized that a world without Taylor Swift is no world worth living in! He admits that he likes your music, too (so it's not all about me…). (Not that you need anyone actively recruiting new fans, but if you did, I'm pretty good at it!)

And so, my new friend, Taylor, this is where I'm signing off. I was going to extend an invitation to one of our kickball games…or, if you don't read this in time, one of our dodgeball games…but I cannot imagine a world where Taylor

Swift is standing on the sidelines, and anyone would be able to focus...(funny, given the most recent times I've seen you on TV... Go Chiefs!). At the same time, in my perfect world, you're just saving up whatever's left after your charitable donations so that you can make a...uh...major move, career-wise - once you're constitutionally allowed to - at age 35...wink, wink, nudge, nudge. Because if anyone can save the world, you've got my vote: **Superstar**...**Superman**...Superhero.

Anyway, you're the best.

PS- In my fantasy land where we actually meet in person someday, please don't judge me if I am one of those people who loses my ability to form sentences. I've already forgiven myself for the inevitable.

Thank you for everything.

Stay...stay...stay tuned for an explanation of how you inevitably got so woven into my writing that there was no stopping it once it started...

All my love,

-*Bruce*

CHAPTER 63

•••••••• • ••••••••

A Perfect Storm…of Creativity.

Jon and I had our pool house blow out Labor Day weekend 2023. I started making the post-it notes for a book about relationships, generally, on September 4th. On September 5th, the following conversation amongst my kickball team members began on our group chat…

Hollis: I cannot believe Panic Point would schedule on the same night as the **ERAS Tour movie** premiere (disgruntled face)

Daniel: The homophobia is real.

Dale: Even The Exorcist knew better.

Hollis: Thank you

Claire: yall tswift fans rlly are too much lmao

Dale: We control the weather

Ashley: Everyday is a panic point in the USA, we need Taylor to get through it!

Dale: This made me cackle

Claire: oct 13 belongs to spook szn activities not tswift

Hollis: GASP

Terry: *clutches pearls*

Ashley: Please do not take the Lord's name in vain

Dale (responding to Claire): VETOED

Daniel: Thank god I just popped some pop corn for this entertainment.

Dale (still responding to Claire): You are the weakest link

Mitchell (responding to Claire): Couldn't agree more, @Claire (heart)

Hollis (responding to Claire): That's Dr. Taylor Swift for you (laughing face, clapping hands)

Terry: We should totally have all of our Swifties do a Taylor Swift costume contest for our Halloween party.

Dale: When did we decide on a Halloween Party?

Ashley: This Swiftie will be in Ireland BUT I would love to do an end of season eras party…haha

Mitchell (responding to Hollis): I couldn't find her doctoral information…..

Dale (responding to Terry): I'm in

Zach: I'm on board with @Claire

Claire: (6 laughing faces) mitch I love you lmao

Dale: And I thought we really bonded at the pool party, **alls well that ends well** I guess

Zach: @Daniel is getting the popcorn I'm grabbing a whiteclaw for this blowout (laughing tears face)

Mitchell (responding to Claire): (3 laughing tears faces)

Terry: Y'all are a trip

Claire (responding to Dale): let our love break all the rules despite our differences (3 hands making hearts)

Dale: Look now, I bet you couldn't find much on her anymore, Taylor Swift lets us know what Taylor Swift wants us to know.

Claire: Smart (cookie)

Ashley: I don't think we need to fight. Mariah owns Christmas. Taylor can own Halloween. Everyone wins.

Mitchell: Taylor is definitely scary enough to own Halloween. I agree.

Claire: HAAAAA

Zach: I'm dead (laughing tears face)

Hollis: Take it back!

Dale: Let's take it easy now, she owns **red, 1989** (now), **august** and the year **22**

Terry: Wonder who's gonna be the villain in **eras**

Hollis: Everyone will be after Mitchell (3 laughing tear faces)

Ashley: I'm just going to **shake it off.**

Dale: **Haters gonna hate**

Zach: And I'm feeling **22** (emotionless face)

Dale: Never ever cross a Swiftie's OR Taylor Swifts path in any wrong doing, if you learn anything from us just know we are crazy and unhinged and we move mountains

Tom: If I can't make it to panic point...**say you'll remember me?**

Dale: Only in my **wildest dreams**

Claire (responding to Dale, 2 msgs back): pshht

Ashley: It's ok Dale. He is joking. He would never talk badly about mother.

Dale: And then **the sinking feeling starts**

Mitchell (responding to Hollis): Bring it (winky face, winky tongue-out face)

Ashley (responding to Zach): This play fight has me feeling 13. I feel like I should be updating my Myspace account to take Mitchell out of my top 8. (laughing tears face)

Dale: He's been removed in my head already

Hollis (responding to Mitchell): And we only just met and here we are now – **Are you ready for it???**

Zach: I could tell @Mitchell was the **trouble** maker (laughing with tears)

Ashley: **I knew** he was **trouble when** he **walked in.**

Mitchell: No

Bruce: I stumbled into this chat tonight...**The air was cold**...(freezing face)

Ashley (responding to Bruce): (2 laughing tears faces, 2 shy blushing faces)

Dale (responding to Bruce): I won't have a choice but to remember **all too well**

Ashley: Y'all Mitchell is really good at kickball, and he has that **James Dean daydream look in** his **eyes**...

Chase: Too long didn't read. What's happening?

Mitchell: ....not this

Dale: Please join me every Sunday as I belt **All Too Well** [at karaoke]

Mitchell: Is that a song?

Ashley (responding to Chase): **Run**!! Save yourself.

Dale (responding to Mitchell): Bye

Dale: *dale left the chat*

Dale: (3 red scarfs)

Hollis: (3 frustrated faces)

Zach: (3 laughing tears faces)

Bruce: When I left the cookout I was thinking **"today was a fairytale…"**. When did we become so divided? (teeth clinched face)

Dale: Lmao I love this team

Bruce: Let's make this season a **love story** y'all!

Claire: Bruce I am so tired of you (7 laughing sideways with tears faces)

Mitchell: (GIF of a man dry heaving)

Zach: Here I am listening to Metallica while you guys are still on this **Taylor Swift** subject (shrugging man)

Dale (responding to Bruce): It's **gonna** last **forever** or **go down in flames**

Mitchell: Definitely flames (flame emoji)

Bruce (responding to Claire): (GIF of Taylor, **Haters Gonna Hate**)

Hollis (responding to Zach): Oh she's not the subject. She's the entire curriculum. (clapping hands)

Ashley: Clearly Mitchell's favorite artist is John Mayer.

Dale (responding to Zach): Just cause I listen to Taylor doesn't mean I don't appreciate the classics

Mitchell: (GIF of Taylor slipping and falling on stage)

{**shots fired**}

Dale (responding to Mitchell): And she still ate the entire performance

Mitchell: Hmm…But did she, thoughhh?

Zach: Only if I could mute when Taylor swift comes up

Dale (responding to Mitchell): Did you watch the performance or the entire show?

Bruce: We all come back on the playing field following an injury, when it makes sense. Why you gotta be an **anti-hero** Mitchell? I used to think you were **bejeweled**

Ashley: (GIF of a woman saying, "I think sometimes people are really mean to the hot, popular girl.")

Dale (responding to Bruce): Plssssssss

Dale: Bruce is out of control (3 laughing with tears faces)

Bruce (in response to his own message): (Ok no we don't, but she would. *heart emoji* TS)

Claire (in response to Dale): someone cut his circuit wiring

Bruce: I just opened tonight's hate charade and don't know why people hate someone who is throwing $$ brief cases at their bus drivers? I mean, I'm not…(teeth clinched face)

Ashley: Nothing wrong with Bruce! He is **end game**

Bruce: **A-team**!

Dale (responding to Bruce, 2 msgs ago): Such a humble and generous queen

Dale: Ok ok ok we are done, goodnight everyone!

Bruce: Good call! Mitchell, I know **you're not sorry** but I love you anyways (laughing sideways tears face, kissing w/ heart face)

Mitchell: Love you too, boo (purple heart)

Bruce: Claire, I love you **forever and always**…(but does he mean the words…or the spirit of the song…hmm (deep in thought face)). Ok I'm done xoxo

Hollis: This absolute nonsense was amazing

Melissa, our team's co-captain, chimed in: I spent my night in a **lavender haze** and just caught up on the chaos.

Then Terry, our team's captain, ended it: I just caught up on yesterdays chat. That was amazing.

BRUCE LANGDON

CHAPTER 64

•••••••••••••••

Right where you left me

**Friends break up...friends get married...
Strangers get born...strangers get buried.**
    -**Right where you left me**, Taylor Swift

Unlike the lyrics, in some instances, it was the friends that got buried and not strangers.

One of the harder parts of writing the original book, <u>Better Man</u>, was realizing how many people have died along the way. And each of them was uniquely awesome, which is what made it so difficult to reflect upon the fact that they aren't here anymore. The following is a tribute to those people who had an impact on my story but who aren't here to read it...

Trey McCaskill

The first person who was mentioned in the book but who is no longer with us is "Trey." Trey McCaskill died at 39 years old – but what's more important is how he lived when he was here. Trey was a super sweet guy with an incredible smile. He was kind. He was handsome. And if you were over at his house long enough, he was going to make you watch his clogging videos. That may not sound exciting, but he was excited about it, and he was incredibly talented.

The first time I met Trey, I had gone over to his house with Rob. The three of us were hanging out, along with a couple of other guys. Music was playing. We were having a good time, just enjoying the moment. We were all in one of the bedrooms when there was a knock at the door, which I barely heard over the music. Some confused looks were exchanged, with the shared thought (I guessed) being, "...are we expecting anyone..?" No one was jumping up to check the front door, so I figured I'd at least go and see if anyone was there...(*keep in mind, I had never been to this house, and I did not know Trey well enough to be 'playing bouncer' at his front door...). This is when I learned that being helpful *isn't* always being as helpful as you'd intended it to be. I hesitantly opened Trey's front door, halfway expecting the knocks to have been beats from the club music that was blaring. Or perhaps I'd simply been hearing things... So I was a bit startled when there was a skinny white dude **on the other side of the door** impatiently looking at me.

"Hi...can I help you?..." I asked. He pretty much pushed past me into the house.

"Do you...uh...know Trey?..." I inquired.

The dude replied, "Who is Trey?"

At that moment, I looked behind me and saw Trey had stepped into the living room to see what the hell was going on. Trey's eyes got big, and I was confused. More so than that, I was worried because Trey's face read that I had really messed up by letting this dude in.

"Trey...do you know this guy?"

"I have no idea who *that* is..." Fuck, I had just let some random dude into Trey's house late at night. I'm sure my face reflected that I was freaking out...I knew I was never getting invited back...

That's when Trey and Mack – the skinny dude – busted out laughing.

Holy shit - for a split second there, I thought I had invited a serial killer into the house. Lucky for me, Mack was the boyfriend of one of the two other guys who were over at the house that night. He and Trey knew each other, apparently quite well. Well enough to play a joke on me, the unsuspecting idiot whose heart had stopped for a couple of seconds before they'd erupted with laughter.

CLOSURE

I miss Trey. A lot of people miss Trey, I have no doubt. Because in his 39 years on this earth, a lot of people had come to know and love Trey. (Or, as Rob called him, Trey-ler...lol)

His Celebration of Life ceremony was held at Wrightsville Beach on March 9th, 2019. There was speculative chatter regarding how he died, and to this day, I haven't heard an official statement from anyone who could tell me definitively. Someone said his dad had passed away recently, and that had been really hard on him because they were close. His obituary simply noted that he'd passed away "unexpectedly."

I hadn't spoken to Trey in a couple of years leading up to his death. That makes me incredibly sad that I got too caught up in life to check-in. I had moved to a new city and had kind of left a lot of people in my rearview mirror – for reasons that had nothing to do with them individually. The lesson I'd like to take from this is: if someone is special to you (...to me...) and they fall out of touch – reach out! I am terrible at keeping up with people, and I rarely call anyone unless I have a specific reason. But I would've called without hesitation if I'd known Trey would be gone soon. While I do not actually know if Trey's death was preventable, just letting him know how much I'd missed him since moving away and laughing about old times would've been worth taking a few minutes out of my day to check-in.

If I could give 'homework' to anyone reading this text right now, I'd say: Call someone you miss right now and let them know you were thinking of them. Because if something beautiful can come out of something so tragic, I believe Trey would want that. So, make someone's day brighter – Trey's smile always did.

Eric Redolphy

Eric Redolphy is described in the original book I wrote as "wise" because when I think back on the things he said…well…he just was. I hated changing his name for the original book ("Erik Blitzen") because I wanted him to be credited for the insightful things he said. And more than that, how much love he and his husband shared gave me and many of our friends a great deal of hope that we, too, could find one person we wanted to be with and be happy. I don't pretend to know anything about their relationship aside from what I saw first-hand, but what I witnessed was two guys who looked at each other **like the stars that shined, in the sky, the pretty lights…** They were noticeably happier when the other walked into the room, even after years of being together. They had nicknames that I don't know the backstory to at all, but calling each other "P" and "B" seemed to make them both smile even bigger.

Eric had the raspiest voice I have ever heard come out of a human being's mouth. I can still hear it when I stop and think about it. And it makes me smile. Because Eric also had, from my perspective, a **perfectly good heart**. I say it like that because Eric had a protective nature, and I don't remember anything about him that was short of perfectly good. His protectiveness was most evident in the way he spoke about and spoke to his partner. It was also very evident with his friends. When I dated Kris, Kris called Eric his best friend. In the specific moments I remember Eric sharing thoughts or his personal observations with me directly, I believe he wanted me to understand a deeper message behind his words. I don't remember him speaking ill of anyone, but he would give insight into people he felt could be problematic. I was NOT that deep of a thinker at the time, but I get it now. **The moment I knew** came way late, but I picked up what he was putting down, eventually. More retrospectively, really. But better late than never.

CLOSURE

Eric lost his 2-year battle with lung cancer in 2015. He was 50 years old.

Sam (*aka "Tommy" from Better Man)

Sam was Jon's older brother. There's a lot about Sam's story that would not be my place to even try to tell. So, I am going to limit this to my personal experience, along with things that Jon told me directly about his brother.

Sam was absolutely hilarious. He was witty in a way that was unmatched. He came to live on Jon's property – specifically, in the apartment above Jon's (former) office, in a building that was detached from the main house.

Sam could make anyone laugh. 'Til their sides hurt. We were out at the nightclub one night, up in a room called 'the caboose.' This was easily the most memorable time I remember being around him. Specifically, because it was this night that I nicknamed him "Captain Crazy" – an oddly fitting nickname that he took no offense to. You know how people describe others as "ridiculously funny" sometimes? Well, Sam was as ridiculous as he was funny. I remember having the thought that he was as funny as Rodney Dangerfield, not to mention (– at least from my perspective –) they had similar mannerisms…and I'll just say it: they bore a slight resemblance to one another. (*I am well aware that isn't necessarily a compliment, but sitting in the caboose that night, I absolutely felt their similarities outweighed any differences.) Captain Crazy had us all roaring with laughter.

There are stories Jon told me that, like I mentioned, aren't mine to tell. I *could* recall them, but it would be very tricky for me to do so in a manner that felt like it accurately represented Jon's older brother. Because these were Jon's retellings of Sam's stories, not ones that I was there to witness.

What I will say is this: Jon could tell stories about Sam, and the words by themselves may leave someone thinking, "Wow, Sam did some things that his family members probably weren't too happy about..." – but to hear Jon describe these events – with his tone, inflection, body language and the fact that he was cackling throughout the stories - it suggested that Jon had not only forgiven Sam but that he had completely gotten over any negative vibes that may've once existed. Jon found Sam's craftiness far more impressive and worth much more than the value of anything Sam may have stolen. Jon shared these memories with me before Sam passed away, so it's not like Jon was holding a grudge and only forgave Sam after he was gone, either. In fact, it was despite Sam's past bad behavior that Jon moved him into the garage apartment. It was evident that Jon loved his older brother very much, and there was nothing Sam had ever stolen that Jon couldn't spin into a hilarious story and get a lot of laughs from. Jon didn't want to encourage Sam's thieving, but he did admit to me that he was impressed by some of Sam's more inventive ways of finagling his way into locked spaces or safes. The only problem was that Sam eventually ended up telling on himself. Often, when he was in the clear and the questioning had stopped...Sam would admit it. If for even a second Jon wanted to believe 'maybe-Sam-*really-didn't*-do-it-after-all...', that was when Sam would flip-script: alright! Alright! I admit it...it was me!... Jon knew it had been...but he spoke with a level of admiration over Sam's dedication to taking the lie to the finish line - even if he did stop just short, only to admit the truth (...along with how he'd managed to pull it off. It sounded like there was some level of pride Sam took in owning just how clever he was.).

[[**Sam's appearances in the <u>Better Man</u> book are limited to his tragic death and an urn story. It didn't feel fair to leave it at that, given that there was plenty more to Sam than simply that he died. But again, any other stories aren't mine to tell...]]

CHAPTER 65

•••••••• • •••••••••

This 1 is for my true Swifties:

To summarize each of the significant relationships from both books and how I feel about them after all has been reflected upon, typed out, and sent to press...

*Honestly, Taylor Swift fans could probably just skip reading **Better Man** and **Closure** completely and get the gist by reviewing this list...

Kris McCray: **Daylight. Paper Rings. Last Kiss.**

Jon: **Would've, Could've, Should've. Tolerate It. The Moment I Knew. closure.**

Nathan: **I did something bad. Now That We Don't Talk.**

Nick: **the 1**

William: a**ugust. Hits Different.**

After-kickball-in-the-club kisser (unnamed): **Say Don't Go**

Big Kick Energy (BKE – my kickball team): **Long Live!** (with an Honorable Mention of **this is me trying**)

Chad: **Teardrops on My Guitar. I'd lie.** *that was a toss-up / close call...

Huh?...but...?...I'm confused...

CHAPTER 66

•••••••• • •••••••

To Summarize...

...*WAIT!*...

...Who's *Chad?*...?...

A wise woman once sang **the greatest of luxuries is your secrets**. So, **dear reader**, I'm keeping that to myself...

& to Chad: I will not write anything about you in a book after this, ever...You have my word. (*if you'd like to see the page(s) I already wrote about you but then pulled, I will show them to you...we'll call 'em **words that** were **whispered, for just us to know**...)

Ok, now for the summary...

Without pointing fingers, I let the way I felt about myself, internally, after my relationship with Jon derail any potential for other relationships to pan out for a long time. I tried to block the relationship out of my mind altogether and move on. But this came with consequences. I didn't let Nick know I once had feelings for him until 5 years later – when I wrote about him in this book. (And he confirmed he had no idea I felt that way back then.) I royally fucked up anything romantic that ever could have been with William by being a drunken idiot. (*Thanks, Taylor, for normalizing bottles of wine slipping away...#**august**.) And Nathan sent out every red flag under the sun right off the bat. But I still dated him.

I recognize now that what I needed more than anything in the aftermath of Jon was therapy. Because truly, my sense of self was non-existent after that relationship. **I'd like to be my old self again, but I'm still trying to find it**...*that* is precisely what I am trying to say here. It's hard to remember joking with people that "I suffer from *high* self-esteem" many years ago. That feels like another lifetime. Because present-day..? As insignificant as being kissed by a cute guy in a nightclub was to me at one point in time, ever since it happened more recently, I've been racking my brain, wondering *why me?* Not in the I'm-a-'victim'-of-those-lips kind of way, but in the why-was-this-cute-guy-interested-in-*me (?)* kind of way. It reminds me of when I told myself Nick would never be interested. So, I never took the risk and gave Nick that embarrassing letter I should have shared back when it was relevant. But when I sent him the screenshot all these years later, it opened up a conversation that ultimately left me with more in the self-esteem bank than I had before I shared it with him. And that feels good.

At the risk of sounding like I'm going back on what I said about he-who-I-swore-I'd-never-write about again, typing out what I did at the top of this chapter is a big deal. I'm not letting *that guy* become the 'new Nick.' And it's not even about whether or not **sparks fly**. It's about finally feeling healed enough to put myself out there! Because I'm not getting trapped in a loop of he'd-never-be-interested-anyway...that **'right-where-you-left-me** thinking' that has continued to infect my life in ways I hadn't recognized until now. Writing all of this out has helped me to identify the flawed thought patterns that have continued to tear me down and hold me back. And it's helped me to recognize I'm NOT there anymore. I'm no longer **sitting at the restaurant**...And I'm beginning to see that there's hope **on the other side of the door.**

*Suggested listen: **Right where you left me** -Taylor Swift

As I was writing out the end of that last paragraph and the next, this little number came on...

*Suggested follow-up: **Enchanted** -Taylor Swift

So, I knew I was on the right track.

I'm finally starting to feel like the hopeless romantic I was at the beginning of **Better Man** is still here. It wasn't just a phase I outgrew, like I was thinking it was when I

219

started writing this book. Nope, he's not **dead and gone and buried.** He just got lost...*I* just got lost...for a very long time. I'm sure I could have found myself sooner had I gone and unleashed all of this on a therapist. But hindsight is 20/20.

No matter the path I had to take to get here, I'm just really glad to be here now. I don't want to be with someone ever again because they **tolerate it.**

I officially haven't seen Jon in a dream now in many months. I'm happy to report I'm not **haunted** by anyone else I've dated...or crushed on in silence...either.

All things considered, I feel like I can say with some confidence that I got what I came for.

#closure

Made in the USA
Columbia, SC
01 June 2024

36504157R00136